Plan # 51020 p.10

Plan # 97714 p.16

single-level
HOME PLANS
9th edition

A collection of 300 of our finest and most popular single-level residential designs, hand selected from the portfolios of award-winning architects and designers across the country.

the
Garlinghouse
company

Plan # 99487 p.14

Plan # 51021 p.11

the Garlinghouse company

We've got your plan.

Single-Level Home Plans, 9th Edition

James D. McNair III, CEO & Publisher
Steve Culpepper, Editorial Director
Debbie Cochran, Managing Editor
Gia C. Manalio, Associate Editor
Christopher Berrien, Art Director
Debra Novitch, Art Production Manager
Andy Russell, Melani Gonzalez, Production Artists

Covers & Interior layouts by Andy Russell

Submit all Canadian plan orders
to the following address:
Garlinghouse Company, 102 Ellis Street, Penticton, BC V2A 4L5
Canadian orders only: 1-800-361-7526
Fax: 1-250-493-7526
Customer Service: 1-250-493-0492

Library of Congress: 00-136079
ISBN: 1-893536-05-X

Table of Contents

Plan 93183 p.26

Wide-open and Convenient

Above A soaring gable adds height to the facade of this lovely single-level home, highlighted by such charming details as the Palladian window and the ginger-bread brackets of the porch columns.

Stacked windows fill the wall in the front bedroom of this one-level home, creating an attractive facade. Around the corner, two more bedrooms and two full baths complete the bedroom wing, set apart for bedtime quiet. Look at the high, sloping ceilings in the living room, the sliders that unite the breakfast room and kitchen with an adjoining deck, and the vaulted ceilings in the formal dining room off the foyer.

REAR ELEVATION

Plan 20100

Price Code	B
Total Finished	1,737 sq. ft.
Main Finished	1,737 sq. ft.
Basement Unfinished	1,727 sq. ft.
Garage Unfinished	484 sq. ft.
Dimensions	72'4"x43'
Foundation	Basement
	Crawlspace
	Slab
Bedrooms	3
Full Baths	2
Main Ceiling	8'
Roof Framing	Stick
Exterior Walls	2x6

Photography by John Ehrenclou

MAIN FLOOR

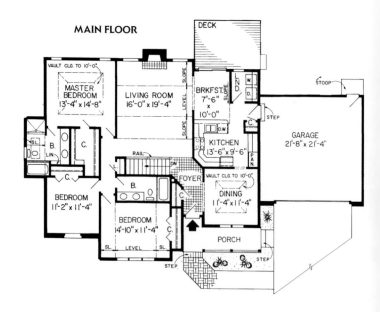

Perfect Compact Ranch

Above The elongated, wraparound style of this home gives it the appearance of reaching out and welcoming family and friends. This warm and inviting feeling continues on the inside with large rooms and centralized community areas.

REAR ELEVATION

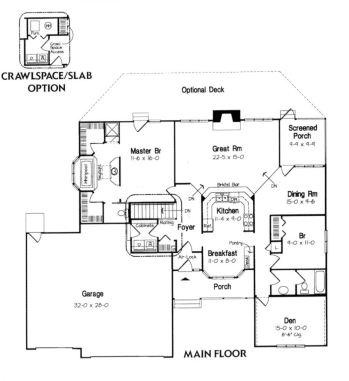

CRAWLSPACE/SLAB OPTION

This Ranch home features a large, centralized sunken great room, with a cozy fireplace. The master bedroom has an unforgettable bathroom with a super skylight. The huge three-car plus garage can include a work area for the family carpenter. In the center of this home, a kitchen includes an eating nook for family gatherings. The porch at the rear of the house is easily accessed from the dining room. One other bedroom and a den, which can easily be converted to a bedroom, are on the opposite side of the house from the master bedroom.

Plan 10839

Price Code	B
Total Finished	1,738 sq. ft.
Main Finished	1,738 sq. ft.
Basement Unfinished	1,083 sq. ft.
Garage Unfinished	796 sq. ft.
Dimensions	66'x52'
Foundation	Basement
	Crawlspace
	Slab
Bedrooms	2
Full Baths	2
Main Ceiling	8'
Roof Framing	Stick
Exterior Walls	2x4, 2x6

Photography by John Ehrenclou

Home with a Heart

Above Pleasant design with clean lines and classic angles work to create nice curb appeal for this family home.

Built around a central core of family activities and functions, this home makes the most of its compact but complete layout. The large kitchen here is clearly the heart of this home, open to the family room with hearth, dining room, and living room. And given its clear view to the entryway, the kitchen also serves as the entry point and welcoming center for guests and visitors.

As a decent-sized family home, this plan has much going for it. Although it contains three full bedrooms and two full baths, it still makes room for a discrete master suite, recognizing the importance of a private, separate place for the adults to relax and disengage. This suite includes a large, long master bath with dressing area, double vanities' and a separate makeup area. The bath includes a large tub and a separate shower as well as a walk-in closet and large standard closet. The bay window off the master suite overlooks the private rear patio, which has access from accompanying French doors off the large bedroom.

Outside of the private master suite, the home unfolds into a true family place where all the functions are central and everything your family needs is right at hand.

Above The homeowner chose to make a modification to this plan's dining room. The modification features a cathedral ceiling and unpainted pine wall and ceiling treatment. The standard plan version of the dining room (shown on page 7) includes a horizontal tray ceiling.

MAIN FLOOR

Below This version of the dining room runs more toward the traditional than the version shown on page 6. Notice the classic inverted tray ceiling detail.

Above The outside door leads onto the patio, virtually expanding this central kitchen into the outdoors. Twin counters (one not shown) fill the kitchen with ample preparation area, also offering space that will work as a serving center for dinner parties or simple family meals. This kitchen has been slightly modified to fit the homeowner's needs.

Plan 10514

Units	Single
Price Code	C
Total Finished	1,980 sq. ft.
Main Finished	1,980 sq. ft.
Garage Unfinished	434 sq. ft.
Dimensions	60'x51'
Foundation	Crawlspace
Bedrooms	3
Full Baths	2
Max Ridge Height	20'
Roof Framing	Stick
Exterior Walls	2x6

Photography by John Erhenclou

Perfectly Detailed

Above Accents and siding variations add to this home's unique exterior appearance. The stepped gables of the entry, mimicking the spaces within, provide a fresh and modern take on an otherwise classic floor plan.

Volume ceilings, a sunken room, and built-in plant shelves are just some of the living details embellishing the inside of this home. All of these features are highlighted by the abundance of windows that seem to surround every room. A fireplace in the living room and one in the country kitchen, providing cozy spaces for family to gather, augment this natural warmth. For more private times, the bedrooms are isolated in the right wing.

Plan 51017

Price Code	C
Total Finished	1,993 sq. ft.
Main Finished	1,993 sq. ft.
Basement Unfinished	1,993 sq. ft.
Garage Unfinished	521 sq. ft.
Dimensions	60'x48'4"
Foundation	Basement
Bedrooms	3
Full Baths	2
Main Ceiling	8'
Max Ridge Height	23'3"
Roof Framing	Truss
Exterior Walls	2x4

Photography Provided by
Bloodgood Plan Services, Inc.

MAIN FLOOR

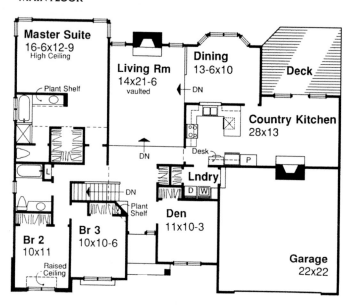

Amenities Everywhere

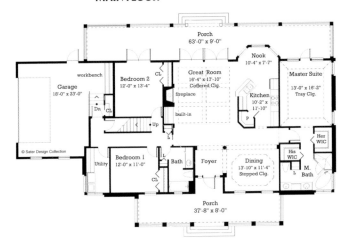

MAIN FLOOR

Porch
63'-0" x 9'-0"

Nook
10'-4" x 7'-7"

workbench

Garage
18'-0" x 23'-0"

Bedroom 2
12'-0" x 13'-4"

Great Room
16'-4" x 17'-10"
Coffered Clg.

fireplace

Master Suite
13'-0" x 16'-2"
Tray Clg.

Kitchen
10'-2" x
11'-10"

built-in

Her
WIC

His
WIC

M.
Bath

© Sater Design Collection

Utility

Bedroom 1
12'-0" x 11'-0"

Bath

Foyer

Dining
13'-10" x 11'-4"
Stepped Clg.

Porch
37'-8" x 8'-0"

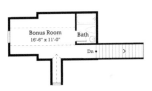

BONUS ROOM

Bonus Room
16'-6" x 11'-0"

Bath

Dn

This home is all about detail and it's this detail, inside and out, that gives it such grand scale. Generously-sized rooms and extended front and back porches provide ample living space. Open community areas promote family activity. On the other hand, the split-bedroom design allows for privacy when it's sought. Elegance abounds with French doors defining the back of the home and columns defining the boundaries of the dining room.

Plan 64173

Price Code	H
Total Finished	1,989 sq. ft.
Main Finished	1,989 sq. ft.
Bonus Unfinished	274 sq. ft.
Garage Unfinished	525 sq. ft.
Dimensions	81'x50'
Foundation	Crawlspace
Bedrooms	3
Full Baths	2
Max Ridge Height	27'
Exterior Walls	2x6

*Alternate foundation options available at an additional charge, call 1-800-235-5700 for more information.

Homey Habitat

Above Great things come in single-level packages and this home packs an abundance of living space into just over 1,200 square feet.

Family-friendly describes this design with its open community areas and core of bedrooms. The vaulted ceilings topping the master bedroom and living and dining areas add grand scale. Designed for the growing family, or one that expects a lot of overnight guests, a den can be easily converted into a third bedroom. A corner of windows, large closet, and private bath make an impressive master suite, as a corner of windows and ample closet space spruce up the second bedroom.

Plan 51020

Price Code	A
Total Finished	1,252 sq. ft.
Main Finished	1,252 sq. ft.
Basement Unfinished	1,252 sq. ft.
Garage Unfinished	420 sq. ft.
Dimensions	44'8"x50'8"
Foundation	Basement
Bedrooms	3
Full Baths	2
Main Ceiling	8'
Max Ridge Height	21'6"
Roof Framing	Truss
Exterior Walls	2x4

Photography Provided by
Bloodgood Plan Services, Inc.

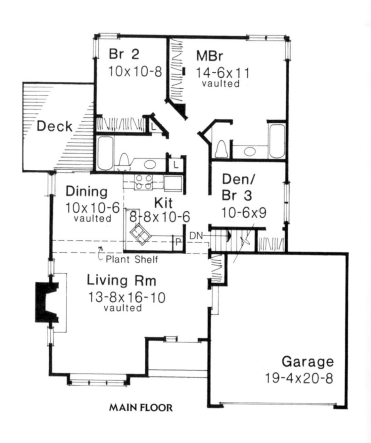

MAIN FLOOR

Subtle Elegance

Above Within this pleasingly simple exterior lies a wealth of generous, well planned living space.

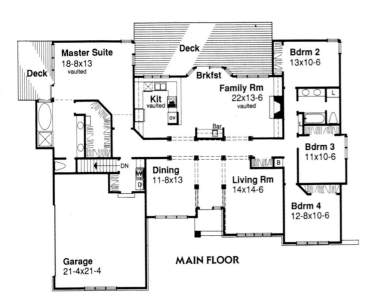

MAIN FLOOR

Columns line the entry, defining the boundaries of the dining room, living room, family room, and kitchen area. Once inside, there is easy access from the family room and breakfast nook to the built-in bar. Ample counter space and a vaulted ceiling define the kitchen. In the right wing, a long hallway unites three secondary bedrooms, while the master suite enjoys the privacy of the left wing, as well as a private deck.

Plan 51021

Price Code	E
Total Finished	2,472 sq. ft.
Main Finished	2,472 sq. ft.
Basement Unfinished	2,472 sq. ft.
Garage Unfinished	544 sq. ft.
Dimensions	73'x56'4"
Foundation	Basement
Bedrooms	4
Full Baths	2
Main Ceiling	8'
Max Ridge Height	22'3"
Roof Framing	Truss
Exterior Walls	2x4

Photography Provided by
Bloodgood Plan Services, Inc.

Single-level Luxury

Above Graceful gables accent the front entry, which is accompanied by a small, elegant porch. To the right is a discrete two-car garage.

At over 2,200 square feet, this home offers single-level luxury that's complete in every respect. From its elegant window details, to its large kitchen with attached breakfast area, three bedrooms (with an optional fourth), and two-car garage, this traditionally detailed home is just right for a family with children or for an couple who want room to entertain and put up overnight guests.

The spaces are magnificently designed for maximum livability and practical function. Bedrooms orbit the main living areas, such as the kitchen/breakfast area, living room, and formal dining room. In the front, a study could be used as a guest room, fourth bedroom, or even a spacious home office for the telecommuter.

The master suite features a spacious bedroom with deep tray ceiling and a complete master bath, comprising a large soaking tub, separate shower, discrete water closet, and double vanities and walk-in closets.

A large fireplace warms the living room and with glass on either side (one window, one window-adorned door), the view across the patio could be of your own carefully tended garden.

Above An expansive deck flows off the living room. Fire up the barby and invite your friends and family over for a cook-out.

Above Toward the right of this living room photo is the foyer; the door toward the left leads into the kitchen.

MAIN FLOOR

- Deck 37'x 6'
- Porch 21'2"x 8'
- Breakfast 11'10"x 11'
- Master Bath
- Master Bedroom 14'6"x 18'4"
- Walk-In Closet
- Living 22'x 17'
- Kitchen 11'10"x 12'
- Utility
- Bath
- Bedroom 11'8"x 12'6"
- Foyer
- Dining 14'10"x 12'
- Bath
- Bedroom 11'4"x 12'
- Porch
- Courtyard
- Three Car Garage 21'4"x 34'8"

Below Looking back from the living room, we see the formal dining room, which in this case has been built with columns separating the large spaces.

Above A quiet, sun-filled corner of the kitchen is given over to the breakfast nook, just right for quiet family meals. For more formal occasions, there's the dining room toward the front of the home.

Plan 94676

Price Code	D
Total Finished	2,201 sq. ft.
Main Finished	2,201 sq. ft.
Garage Unfinished	853 sq. ft.
Porch Unfinished	240 sq. ft.
Dimensions	71'10"x66'10"
Foundation	Slab
Bedrooms	3
Full Baths	3
Main Ceiling	9'
Max Ridge Height	30'9"
Roof Framing	Stick
Exterior Walls	2x4

Photography by Chris A. Little

Defining Columns

Above A practical layout, combined with exquisite details, makes this home a dream come true. The beautifully crafted facade is just a glimpse of what awaits inside.

Columns and arched transoms are focal points of this Ranch home elevation. The 10-foot entry has formal views of the dining room and the great room which features a brick fireplace. The large island kitchen offers an angled range and a pantry. The separate bedroom wing provides optimum privacy. The master suite includes a whirlpool bath with a sloped ceiling, double vanity, and walk-in closet.

Plan 99487

Price Code	C
Total Finished	1,806 sq. ft.
Main Finished	1,806 sq. ft.
Garage Unfinished	548 sq. ft.
Dimensions	55'4"x56'
Foundation	Basement
	Slab
Bedrooms	3
Full Baths	2
Main Ceiling	8'
Roof Framing	Stick/Truss
Exterior Walls	2x4

*Alternate foundation options available at an additional charge, call 1-800-235-5700 for more information.

Photography Provided by
Design Basics, Inc.

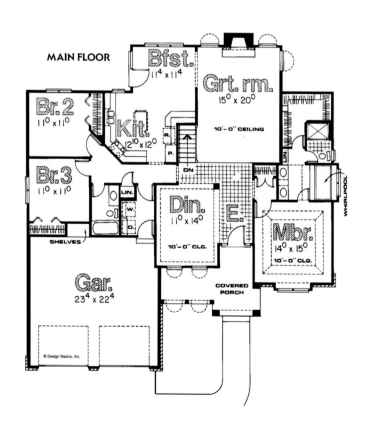

MAIN FLOOR

© Design Basics, Inc.

REAR ELEVATION

This convenient, one-level plan is perfect for the modern family with a taste for classic design. Traditional Victorian touches in this three-bedroom beauty include a romantic, railed porch and an intriguing breakfast tower just off the kitchen. You will love the step-saving arrangement of the kitchen between the breakfast and formal dining rooms. Enjoy the wide-open living room with sliders out to a rear deck and the handsome master suite with its skylit, compartmentalized bath.

Plan 34043

Price Code	B
Total Finished	1,583 sq. ft.
Main Finished	1,583 sq. ft.
Basement Unfinished	1,573 sq. ft.
Garage Unfinished	484 sq. ft.
Dimensions	70'x46'
Foundation	Basement
	Crawlspace
	Slab
Bedrooms	3
Full Baths	2
Main Ceiling	8'
Max Ridge Height	20'
Roof Framing	Stick
Exterior Walls	2x4, 2x6

MAIN FLOOR

Deck (Optional)

Living Rm 15-8 x 17-2 Approx.

MBr 1 14-1 x 15-7

Dining 12-0 x 11-5 Approx.

Kitchen 13-5 x 4-8

Foy

Den/Br 3 10-5 x 11-11

Br 2 10-5 x 11-11

Garage 21-8 x 21-5

Brkfst 10-5 x 9-0

Ldry

CRAWLSPACE/SLAB OPTION

Classic Luxury

Above A bay window to the left and a Palladian window balance the facade of this home, with its curved, sheltered entryway set between them.

It's all about details. The kind of careful details that take into account both architectural tradition and the comfort of people living in the home during this day and age. Tradition and comfort. No wasted lines. No unnecessary square footage. Even from the street, it's clear that this modern masterpiece was designed with care.

Visitors enter through a columned, arched porch, deep enough to shelter guests from the weather, but not so big that the entrance appears showy or out of scale. That understated curve of the porch echoes in the front doorway, a subtle theme of curves that's carried throughout the home.

Built especially for a hilly site, this home keeps the often noisy, active pursuits on the lower level. Because this area is so isolated from the main living areas of the house, guests and kids can enjoy the media room, game room, exercise room, and billiards room whenever they want, getting as loud and raucous as they want. During the day, when the kids are in school, no guests are in the house, and all is quiet, the stage is set for serious work in the downstairs home office.

Above Like a vision from the past, this classic formal dining area next to the foyer creates a special world all its own.

Above Straight from the foyer, guests to your home will head right into the great room, which is subtly separated by a gentle arch and four classic columns.

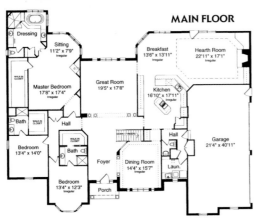

MAIN FLOOR

Dressing

Sitting
11'2" x 7'9"
Irregular

Breakfast
13'6" x 13'11"
Irregular

Hearth Room
22'11" x 17'1"
Irregular

WALK-IN CLOSET

Master Bedroom
17'8" x 17'4"
Irregular

Great Room
19'5" x 17'8"

Kitchen
16'10" x 17'11"
Irregular

Bath

WALK-IN CLOSET

Hall

WALK-IN CLOSET

Bath

DOWN 17 RISERS

Hall

Garage
21'4" x 40'11"

Bedroom
13'4" x 14'0"

Bath

Foyer

Dining Room
14'4" x 15'7"
Irregular

Laun.

Bedroom
13'4" x 12'3"
Irregular

Porch

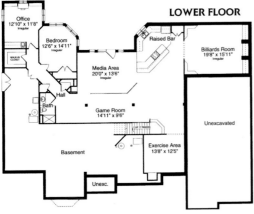

LOWER FLOOR

Office
12'10" x 11'8"
Irregular

Bedroom
12'6" x 14'11"
Irregular

Raised Bar

Billiards Room
19'8" x 15'11"
Irregular

WALK-IN CLOSET

Media Area
20'0" x 13'6"
Irregular

Hall

Bath

Game Room
14'11" x 9'6"

Unexcavated

Basement

Exercise Area
13'8" x 12'5"

Unexc.

Below Look past the breakfast area and into the hearth room, where you can imagine spending many pleasant evenings as dinner simmers on the range and your favorite CD plays in the background while a fire crackles in the hearth.

Above The large island is perfectly positioned to maximize the efficiency of this gourmet kitchen. Notice how the range top is set below the countertop, allowing the top of the counter to shield all the dirty work.

Plan 97714

Price Code	J
Total Finished	3,570 sq. ft.
Main Finished	3,570 sq. ft.
Bonus Unfinished	2,367 sq. ft.
Lower Unfinished	1,203 sq. ft.
Porch Unfinished	50 sq. ft.
Dimensions	84'6"x69'4"
Foundation	Basement
Bedrooms	3
Full Baths	3
Half Baths	1
Max Ridge Height	30'
Roof Framing	Truss
Exterior Walls	2x4

Photography Provided by
Studer Residential Design, Inc.

Stately Symmetry

F rom the outside in, this plan is the perfect balance of elegance and practicality. The master suite fills the left wing of the home, while the secondary bedrooms fill the other. A private study and an open kitchen/dining area flank the centralized great room. Front and rear porches add to outdoor living, and the rear garage promotes privacy.

MAIN FLOOR

BONUS ROOM

Plan 64194

Price Code	H
Total Finished	2,454 sq. ft.
Main Finished	2,454 sq. ft.
Bonus Unfinished	256 sq. ft.
Garage Unfinished	547 sq. ft.
Dimensions	80'6"x66'6"
Foundation	Crawlspace
Bedrooms	3
Full Baths	2
Max Ridge Height	24'2"
Exterior Walls	2x6

*Alternate foundation options available at an additional charge, call 1-800-235-5700 for more information.

Dramtic Ranch

REAR ELEVATION

A deep front porch running the full width of the house adds to the low, sheltering appeal of this thoughtfully planned design. The large living area has a stone fireplace and decorative beams. The kitchen and dining room lead to an outside deck. The laundry room has a large pantry and is off the eating area. The master bedroom has a wonderful bathroom with a huge walk-in closet. In the front of the house, there are two additional bedrooms with a bathroom. This house offers convenient one floor living with nice big rooms.

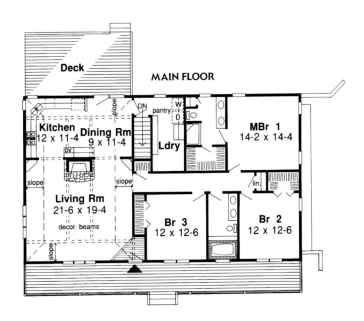

Plan 20198

Price Code	C
Total Finished	1,792 sq. ft.
Main Finished	1,792 sq. ft.
Basement Unfinished	818 sq. ft.
Garage Unfinished	857 sq. ft.
Dimensions	56'x32'
Foundation	Basement
Bedrooms	3
Full Baths	2
Main Ceiling	8'
Max Ridge Height	25'
Roof Framing	Stick
Exterior Walls	2x4, 2x6

Brick and Stucco

This traditional design is accented by the use of gable roofs and the blend of stucco and brick to form a truly spectacular exterior. This home has the look and feel of a much larger home. Entering the den, we find a high vaulted ceiling with built-in cabinets and a fireplace. The dining room is open to the den creating the great room feel for this area. The U-shaped kitchen features built-in appliances. The bedrooms are designed in a split fashion. The master bedroom is located to the rear of the plan and features a private bath.

Plan 92502

Price Code	A
Total Finished	1,237 sq. ft.
Main Finished	1,237 sq. ft.
Garage Unfinished	436 sq. ft.
Dimensions	50'x38'
Foundation	Crawlspace
	Slab
Bedrooms	3
Full Baths	2
Main Ceiling	8'
Max Ridge Height	18'6"
Roof Framing	Stick
Exterior Walls	2x4

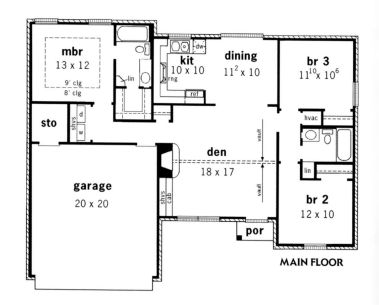

MAIN FLOOR

A Mini Castle

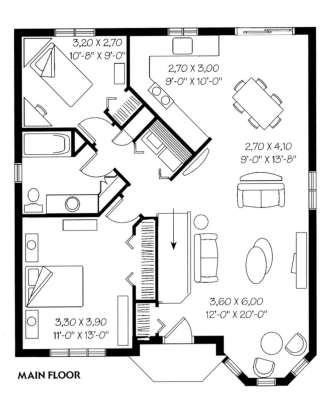

MAIN FLOOR

3,20 X 2,70
10'-8" X 9'-0"

2,70 X 3,00
9'-0" X 10'-0"

2,70 X 4,10
9'-0" X 13'-8"

3,60 X 6,00
12'-0" X 20'-0"

3,30 X 3,90
11'-0" X 13'-0"

Victorian accents grace the facade of this home. Inside, the bedrooms are privately located in the left wing while the open community areas fill the right. A bayed sitting area adds to the living space and the coziness. Ample counter space defines the kitchen and the large dining area features a sliding glass door to the backyard.

Plan 65005

Price Code	A
Total Finished	972 sq. ft.
Main Finished	972 sq. ft.
Basement Unfinished	972 sq. ft.
Dimensions	30'x35'
Foundation	Basement
Bedrooms	2
Full Baths	1
Main Ceiling	8'2"
Max Ridge Height	17'6"
Exterior Walls	2x6

One-level Living

This home features a well designed floor plan, offering convenience and style. The living room includes a two-sided fireplace shared with the dining room. A U-shaped kitchen is equipped with a peninsula counter/breakfast bar. The private master suite includes a whirlpool tub, double vanity, and a step-in shower. A large walk-in closet adds ample storage space to the suite. The secondary bedroom and the den/guest room share use of the full hall bath.

Plan 24701

Price Code	B
Total Finished	1,625 sq. ft.
Main Finished	1,625 sq. ft.
Basement Unfinished	1,625 sq. ft.
Garage Unfinished	455 sq. ft.
Dimensions	54'x48'4"
Foundation	Basement
	Crawlspace
	Slab
Bedrooms	3
Full Baths	2
Main Ceiling	8'-9'
Max Ridge Height	22'
Roof Framing	Stick
Exterior Walls	2x4, 2x6

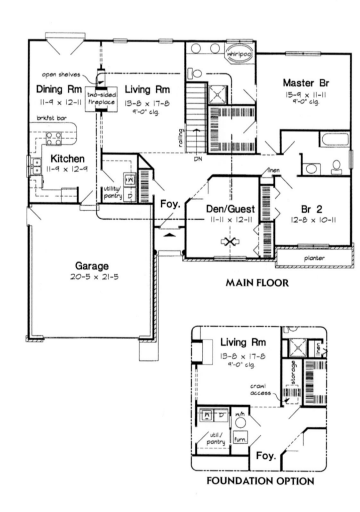

MAIN FLOOR

FOUNDATION OPTION

Two front porches extend living outdoors. Inside, each room is distinctly separated, creating a sense of privacy. Counter space, including a casual eating bar, abounds in the kitchen. A separate dining area, featuring sliding glass doors to the back yard, offers more formal dining. The laundry is tucked privately away in the large full bath.

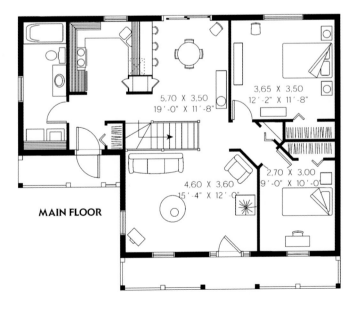

5,70 X 3,50
19'-0" X 11'-8"

3,65 X 3,50
12'-2" X 11'-8"

2,70 X 3,00
9'-0" X 10'-0"

4,60 X 3,60
15'-4" X 12'-0"

MAIN FLOOR

Plan 65006

Price Code	A
Total Finished	920 sq. ft.
Main Finished	920 sq. ft.
Porch Unfinished	152 sq. ft.
Dimensions	38'x28'
Foundation	Basement
Bedrooms	2
Full Baths	1
Main Ceiling	8'
Max Ridge Height	20'6"
Roof Framing	Truss
Exterior Walls	2x6

Extra Touches

Y ou don't have to sacrifice style when buying a smaller home. Notice the Palladian window with a fan light above at the front of the home. The entrance porch includes a turned post entry. Once inside, the living room is topped by an impressive volume ceiling, and accented by a fireplace. A decorative ceiling enhances both the master bedroom and the dining room. A private bath and double closet highlight the master suite.

Plan 24700

Price Code	A
Total Finished	1,312 sq. ft.
Main Finished	1,312 sq. ft.
Basement Unfinished	1,293 sq. ft.
Garage Unfinished	459 sq. ft.
Dimensions	50'x40'
Foundation	Basement
	Crawlspace
	Slab
Bedrooms	3
Full Baths	2
Main Ceiling	8'
Roof Framing	Stick
Exterior Walls	2x6

MAIN FLOOR

Optional
Deck

Reveal Clg.

Mstr Br
12-8 x 11-4

Living Rm
13-0 x 19-4

Reveal Clg.

Dining Rm
10-0 x 11-4

Kitchen
9-8 x 9-4

Flat Clg. @ 12'   Beams Above

Railing

DN

Panltry

Laun.

8' Clg.

Foyer

Optional Door Location

Linen

Br 3/Den
10-0 x 11-4

Garage
20-4 x 21-8

Br 2
10-10 x 10-8

Porch

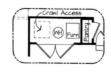

Crawl Access

WH   Furn   Pantry

**CRAWLSPACE/SLAB
OPTION**

Arched Windows

Above An unbelievable amount of living space and convenience is packed into this single-level home. With a room designed for just about every hobby under the sun, there's something here to please every family member.

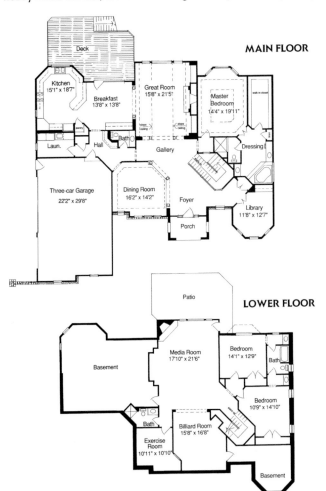

MAIN FLOOR

Deck

Kitchen
15'1" x 18'7"

Breakfast
13'8" x 13'8"

Great Room
15'8" x 21'5"

Master Bedroom
14'4" x 19'11"

walk-in closet

Laun.

Hall

Bath

Gallery

Dressing

Three-car Garage
22'2" x 29'8"

Dining Room
16'2" x 14'2"

Foyer

Porch

Library
11'8" x 12'7"

LOWER FLOOR

Patio

Basement

Media Room
17'10" x 21'6"

Bedroom
14'1" x 12'9"

Bath

Bedroom
10'9" x 14'10"

Bath

Billiard Room
15'8" x 16'8"

Exercise Room
10'11" x 10'10"

Basement

Basement

Detailed stucco and stone accents provide warmth and character to this one-level home. An arched entry invites you into the interior where elegant window styles and dramatic ceiling treatments create an impressive showplace. An extravagant master bedroom suite and library with built-in bookshelves round out the first floor. Two additional bedrooms with a tandem bath, a media room, billiard room, and exercise room are created in the finished basement.

Plan 92657

Price Code	L
Total Finished	4,328 sq. ft.
Main Finished	2,582 sq. ft.
Lower Finished	1,746 sq. ft.
Basement Unfinished	871 sq. ft.
Dimensions	70'8"x64'4"
Foundation	Basement
Bedrooms	3
Full Baths	2
Half Baths	1
3/4 Baths	1
Max Ridge Height	26'5"
Roof Framing	Truss
Exterior Walls	2x4

Photography Provided by
Studer Residential Design, Inc.

Spacious Comfort

Above Lots of windows and clever use of roof shapes create curb appeal on the outside and a cozy, spacious home inside.

The design and layout of this award-winning Ranch is just right for a sloped lot. A full, walk-out basement opening onto the backyard could provide hundreds of additional square feet of living space.

As is, the house is absolutely complete and spacious. The formal foyer seems to invite guests into the comfort of the great room, which lies straight ahead. The open-plan great room has a large fireplace flanked by built-in cabinetry on each side for holding audio-visual equipment, books or even a bar. High ceilings and large windows help wash the space with natural light.

The formal dining room, which is set diagonally from the great room, opens to the rest of the house through an elegant arched entry. A large window set allows natural light to spill inside. The kitchen is a mother's gourmet's dream, with a center island and an abundance of storage space of all kinds.

French doors open into the elegant master bedroom, which features a unique sitting area with bay-window views in three directions. Two walk-in closets, and a private master bath with spa tub, double vanity, and separate shower make this master suite the perfect retreat from a hard day at work. A U-shaped stair leads to the lower level where there is plenty room for recreation, or even more bedrooms.

MAIN FLOOR

Below The great room opens with a large arch supported by massive columns. Inside is a world of light, thanks to the wall of large windows and French doors. Notice the elegant fireplace with arched built-ins flanking either side.

Above The spacious kitchen features tons of storage space, room for a small "command center" desk, and a cleverly angled central kitchen island.

Plan 93183

Price Code	F
Total Finished	2,600 sq. ft.
Main Finished	2,600 sq. ft.
Basement Unfinished	2,600 sq. ft.
Dimensions	87'x60'
Foundation	Basement
Bedrooms	3
Full Baths	2
Half Baths	1
Max Ridge Height	26'8"
Roof Framing	Stick
Exterior Walls	2x6

Photography provided by
Ahmann Design, Inc.

Simply Swell

The covered porch offers an inviting welcome into the home. Inside, the open design of the community areas promotes quality family activity. All bedrooms, each with ample closet space, are isolated for privacy in the right wing. The kitchen offers an eating island for casual dining, while a larger dining area provides additional space for more formal times.

MAIN FLOOR

4.50 X 7.90
15'-0"X 26'-4"

4.50 X 3.60
15'-0"X 12'-0"

4.60 X 3.60
15'-0"X 12'-0"

2.70 X 3.70
9'-0"X 12'-4"

3.60 X 3.10
12'-0"X 10'-4"

3.60 X 3.70
12'-0"X 12'-4"

Plan 65075

Price Code	A
Total Finished	1,176 sq. ft.
Main Finished	1,176 sq. ft.
Basement Unfinished	1,176 sq. ft.
Garage Unfinished	401 sq. ft.
Porch Unfinished	110 sq. ft.
Dimensions	58'x28'
Foundation	Basement
Bedrooms	3
Full Baths	1
Max Ridge Height	18'10"
Roof Framing	Truss
Exterior Walls	2x6

Detailed Charmer

Walk past the charming front porch, in through the foyer and you'll be struck by the exciting, spacious living room, complete with high sloping ceilings and a beautiful fireplace. The large master bedroom has its own private bath and a decorative ceiling. The dining room provides decorative ceiling details and a full slider out to the deck.

MAIN FLOOR

Optional Deck

CRAWLSPACE/SLAB OPTION

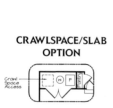

Crawl Space Access

Optional Vault Ceiling

Mbr 1
11-4 x 12-8

Living
13-0 x 19-4

Beams Above

Railing

Decor. Clg.

Dining
10-0 x 11-4

Kitchen
9-6 x 10-0

Railing

DN

Linen

Optional Door

Foyer

Br 3
Den/Study
10-0 x 11-4

Br 2
10-8 x 10-10

Garage
20-5 x 21-8

Railing
Porch

Plan 20161

Price Code	A
Total Finished	1,307 sq. ft.
Main Finished	1,307 sq. ft.
Basement Unfinished	1,298 sq. ft.
Garage Unfinished	462 sq. ft.
Dimensions	50'x40'
Foundation	Basement
	Crawlspace
	Slab
Bedrooms	3
Full Baths	2
Main Ceiling	8'
Max Ridge Height	19'
Roof Framing	Stick
Exterior Walls	2x6

Great Starter Home

This functional, one level plan features a lovely country porch entry into a spacious living room that is accented by a fireplace. The master bedroom includes a private double-vanity bath with a whirlpool tub and separate shower. The two additional bedrooms share a full double-vanity bath which has the added convenience of a laundry center.

Plan 24708

Price Code	B
Total Finished	1,576 sq. ft.
Main Finished	1,576 sq. ft.
Basement Unfinished	1,454 sq. ft.
Garage Unfinished	576 sq. ft.
Porch Unfinished	391 sq. ft.
Dimensions	93'x36'
Foundation	Basement
	Crawlspace
	Slab
Bedrooms	3
Full Baths	2
Main Ceiling	8'
Roof Framing	Stick
Exterior Walls	2x4

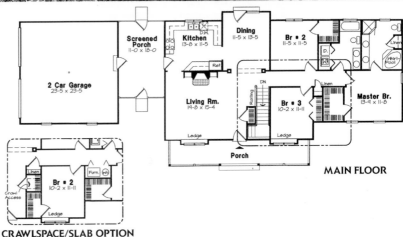

MAIN FLOOR

CRAWLSPACE/SLAB OPTION

Attention to Detail

This spacious four bedroom home features a formal foyer leading directly into the den. The den is expansive, topped by a raised ceiling, and focuses on a cozy fireplace. The kitchen plan includes an angled work area with extended counter that is open to the den and eating area. The split bedroom plan insures privacy for the master bedroom.

Plan 92550

Price Code	F
Total Finished	2,735 sq. ft.
Main Finished	2,735 sq. ft.
Garage Unfinished	561 sq. ft.
Porch Unfinished	273 sq. ft.
Dimensions	68'10"x67'4"
Foundation	Crawlspace
	Slab
Bedrooms	4
Full Baths	3
Main Ceiling	9'
Tray Ceiling	10'
Roof Framing	Stick
Exterior Walls	2x4

MAIN FLOOR

Substantial Storage

This home's elegant facade houses a well laid out floor plan. Perfect for first-time homeowners or a small family, this home provides all the amenities you'll need. Counter and cabinet space surrounds the kitchen, while a focal-point fireplace, flanked by floor-to-ceiling windows, warms the living area. Each bedroom has generous closet space and an additional large closet is located in the hallway.

MAIN FLOOR

Plan 65078

Price Code	A
Total Finished	1,059 sq. ft.
Main Finished	1,059 sq. ft.
Garage Unfinished	300 sq. ft.
Dimensions	38'x46'8"
Foundation	Basement
Bedrooms	2
Full Baths	1
Main Ceiling	8'
Max Ridge Height	17'1"
Roof Framing	Truss
Exterior Walls	2x6

Family Friendly Details

Bumped-out areas define this home's facade, while an atmosphere of community defines within. The entry opens directly into the living area, creating an instant welcome. The open design of the common areas promotes quality family activity. On the other hand, the bedrooms are isolated for more private retreats.

MAIN FLOOR

Plan 65241

Price Code	A
Total Finished	1,068 sq. ft.
Main Finished	1,068 sq. ft.
Basement Unfinished	1,068 sq. ft.
Garage Unfinished	245 sq. ft.
Dimensions	30'8"x48'
Foundation	Basement
Bedrooms	2
Full Baths	1
Main Ceiling	8'
Max Ridge Height	22'1"
Roof Framing	Truss
Exterior Walls	2x6

Pleasant Layout

Above The arches of this home's entrance are a mere introduction to the exquisite features you'll discover inside. From volume ceilings to a whirlpool tub, all within a convenient layout, this plan is rich in detail and appeal.

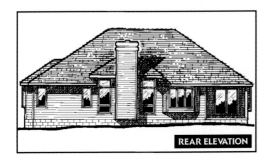

REAR ELEVATION

In the great-room, a focal-point fireplace is flanked by transom windows. The kitchen, dining room, and breakfast area are conveniently located to one another. A corner master suite enjoys a tray ceiling, roomy walk-in closet and a plush bath with double vanity and whirlpool tub.

Plan 94923

Price Code	B
Total Finished	1,666 sq. ft.
Main Finished	1,666 sq. ft.
Basement Unfinished	1,666 sq. ft.
Garage Unfinished	496 sq. ft.
Dimensions	55'4"x48'
Foundation	Basement
Bedrooms	3
Full Baths	2
Max Ridge Height	22'9"
Roof Framing	Stick
Exterior Walls	2x4

*Alternate foundation options available at an additional charge, call 1-800-235-5700 for more information.

Photography Provided by
Design Basics, Inc.

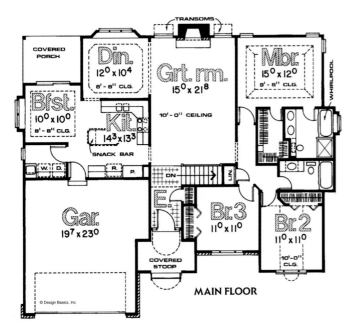

MAIN FLOOR

Warmed by Firelight

The foyer opens directly into the generous living room presenting an instant welcome for family and friends. The fireplace is tucked neatly into the corner of the living room, shedding its glow into the dining room, kitchen, and breakfast area. To the left of the house sit the secondary bedrooms, each with generous closet space and sharing a full bath. The master suite is privately located in the right wing, while a covered porch highlights the back.

MAIN FLOOR

Plan 94610

Price Code	D
Total Finished	2,246 sq. ft.
Main Finished	2,246 sq. ft.
Garage Unfinished	546 sq. ft.
Porch Unfinished	195 sq. ft.
Dimensions	61'-10"x65'-5"
Foundation	Crawlspace
	Slab
Bedrooms	4
Full Baths	2
Half Baths	1
Main Ceiling	9'
Roof Framing	Truss
Exterior Walls	2x4, 2x6

Built to Please

This home is all about convenience. Gorgeous volume ceilings add scale and detail to the master bedroom, dining room, family room, and breakfast nook. Roomy walk-in closets flank the passageway from the master bedroom to the master bath and a built-in desk, generous counter space, and central cooking island make an efficient kitchen.

MAIN FLOOR

BONUS SPACE

Plan 98904

Price Code	F
Total Finished	2,614 sq. ft.
Main Finished	2,614 sq. ft.
Bonus Unfinished	1,681 sq. ft.
Basement Unfinished	2,563 sq. ft.
Garage Unfinished	596 sq. ft.
Porch Unfinished	200 sq. ft.
Dimensions	70'10"x78'9"
Foundation	Basement
Bedrooms	3
Full Baths	2
Half Baths	1
Ridge Height	25'
Roof Framing	Stick
Exterior Walls	2x4

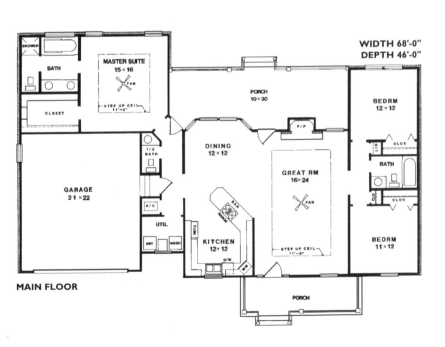

MAIN FLOOR

WIDTH 68'-0"
DEPTH 46'-0"

Attractive Ceilings and Open Layout

Price Code: B

■ This plan features:

— Three bedrooms

— Two full and one half baths

■ Great Room and Master Suite with step-up ceiling treatments

■ Open layout between Kitchen, Dining and Great Room offers a more spacious feeling

■ Five-piece, private Bath and walk-in closet in the pampering Master Suite

■ Two additional Bedrooms located at opposite end of home

■ This home is designed with slab and crawlspace foundation options

MAIN FLOOR — 1,654 SQ. FT.
GARAGE — 480 SQ. FT.

TOTAL LIVING AREA: 1,654 SQ. FT.

Large Living in a Small Space

Price Code: A

■ This plan features:

— Three bedrooms

— One full and one three-quarter baths

■ A sheltered Entry leads into an open Living Room with a corner fireplace and a wall of windows

■ A well-equipped Kitchen features a peninsula counter with Nook, a Laundry, a clothes closet, and a built-in Pantry

■ A Master Bedroom has its own private Bath

■ This home is designed with basement and crawlspace foundation options

MAIN FLOOR — 993 SQ. FT.
GARAGE — 390 SQ. FT.
BASEMENT — 987 SQ. FT.

TOTAL LIVING AREA:
993 SQ. FT.

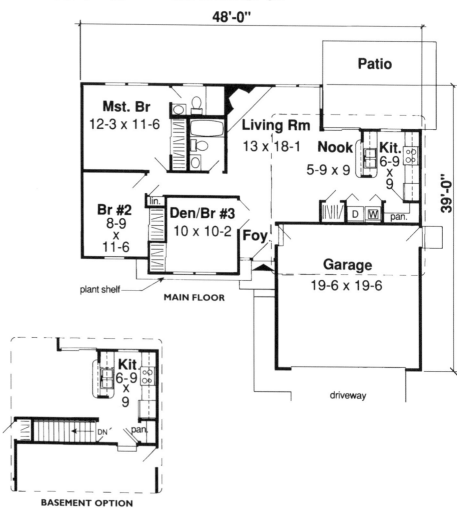

48'-0"

Patio

Mst. Br
12-3 x 11-6

Living Rm
13 x 18-1

Nook
5-9 x 9

Kit.
6-9
x
9

39'-0"

Br #2
8-9
x
11-6

lin.

Den/Br #3
10 x 10-2

Foy

D W pan.

plant shelf

Garage
19-6 x 19-6

MAIN FLOOR

driveway

Kit
6-9
x
9

DN

pan.

BASEMENT OPTION

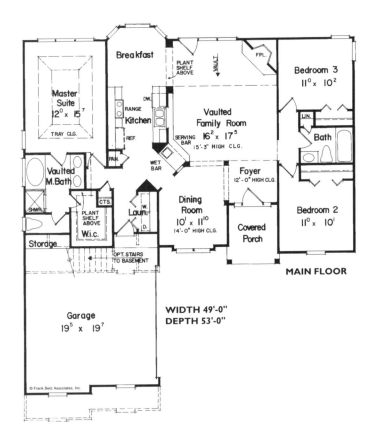

WIDTH 49'-0"
DEPTH 53'-0"

MAIN FLOOR

Split-Bedroom Plan

Price Code: A

■ This plan features:

— Three bedrooms

— Two full baths

■ A tray ceiling gives a decorative touch to the Master Bedroom

■ A full Bath is located between the secondary Bedrooms

■ A corner fireplace and a vaulted ceiling highlight the Family Room

■ A wetbar/serving bar and a Pantry add to the convenience of the Kitchen

■ This home is designed with basement, slab, and crawlspace foundation options

MAIN FLOOR — 1,429 SQ. FT.
BASEMENT — 1,472 SQ. FT.
GARAGE — 438 SQ. FT.

TOTAL LIVING AREA:
1,429 SQ. FT.

Fine Features

Price Code: D

- This plan features:
  — Four bedrooms
  — Two full baths
- Brick, columns, and arched windows give this home an elegant air
- The Master Suite features a 10-foot boxed ceiling in the Bedroom and a luxurious Master Bath with walk-in closet and whirlpool tub
- Details such as a boxed ceiling, French doors, and a fireplace embellish the Great Room
- Columns grace the entrance of the open formal Dining Room
- Ample counter space, including a snack bar, surrounds the Kitchen
- This home is designed with slab or crawlspace foundation options

MAIN FLOOR — 2,148 SQ. FT.
GARAGE — 477 SQ. FT.

TOTAL LIVING AREA:
2,148 SQ. FT.

WIDTH 63'-0"
DEPTH 52'-8"

MAIN FLOOR

© 1999 NELSON DESIGN GROUP, LLC.

Lends Itself to a Corner Lot

Price Code: H

- This plan features:
  — Four bedrooms
  — Three full and one half baths
- Double doors in the Entry lead to a lovely formal Living Room
- The Kitchen is open to a bright mitered glass Nook
- The Master Suite has a cozy Sitting Room and a full Bath with a garden tub
- Two Bedrooms have a walk-in closet and share a full Bath
- There's plenty of storage space throughout this home
- This home is designed with a slab foundation
- Alternate foundation options available at an additional charge. Please call 1-800-235-5700 for more information

MAIN FLOOR — 2,986 SQ. FT.
GARAGE — 574 SQ. FT.

TOTAL LIVING AREA:
2,986 SQ. FT.

MAIN FLOOR

To order your Blueprints, call 1-800-235-5700

Simply Cozy

Price Code: A

■ This plan features:

— Three bedrooms

— Two full baths

■ Quaint front Porch sheltering Entry into the Living Area

■ Formal Dining Room accented with a bay of glass with Sun Deck access

■ Efficient, galley Kitchen with Breakfast Area

■ Secluded Master Bedroom offering a roomy walk-in closet

■ This home is designed with a basement foundation

MAIN FLOOR — 1,325 SQ. FT.
BASEMENT — 556 SQ. FT.
GARAGE — 724 SQ. FT.

TOTAL LIVING AREA:
1,345 SQ. FT.

WIDTH 52'-0"
DEPTH 42'-0"

Sundeck
14-0 x 10-0

© 1996, Jannis Vann & Associates, Inc.

Dw.

Brkfst.
8-2 x 8-2

Kit.
10-0 x 8-2

Dining
11-10 x 10-0

MAIN FLOOR

Bdrm.3
10-0 x 11-6

W. D.

Ref.

Cts.

Built in Cab.

Bth.2

Sky Lt.

Master Bdrm.
10-8 x 16-10

M. Bath

Lin.

Dn.

Living Area
13-8 x 15-0
Flat Ceil. 12-9 High

Vaulted Ceil.

Bdrm.2
13-6 x 11-2

Front Porch

PLAN NO. 97600

Low-Maintenance Facade

Price Code: A

- This plan features:
  — Three bedrooms
  — Two full baths
- The stucco exterior won't require a fresh coat of paint for years to come
- The Laundry Room is conveniently located near the Master Bedroom
- The Foyer opens to the Family Room, which features a vaulted ceiling and fireplace
- This home is designed with basement and crawlspace foundation options

MAIN FLOOR — 1,361 SQ. FT.
BASEMENT — 1,359 SQ. FT.
GARAGE — 530 SQ. FT.

TOTAL LIVING AREA:
1,361 SQ. FT.

WIDTH 49'-6"
DEPTH 45'-4"

MAIN FLOOR

© Frank Betz Associates, Inc.

BASEMENT STAIR LOCATION OPTION

PLAN NO. 92156

Spectacular Views

Price Code: F

- This plan features:
  — Four bedrooms
  — Two full and one three-quarter baths
- Creates an indoor/outdoor relationship with terrific Decks and large glass expanses
- Family Room and Living Room enjoy highly glassed walls taking in the vistas
- Living Room is enhanced by a cathedral ceiling and a warm fireplace
- Dining Room and Kitchen are in an open layout with a center cooktop island/snack bar highlighting the Kitchen
- Master Bedroom enhanced by floor-to-ceiling windowed area, allowing natural light to filter in
- Secondary Bedroom in close proximity to full Bath on main floor
- Two additional Bedrooms, a three-quarter Bath and a Family Room complete the lower level
- This home is designed with a basement foundation

MAIN FLOOR — 1,707 SQ. FT.
LOWER FLOOR — 901 SQ. FT.

TOTAL LIVING AREA:
2,608 SQ. FT.

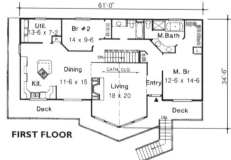

FIRST FLOOR

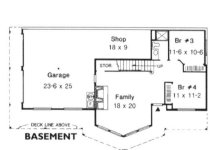

BASEMENT

To order your Blueprints, call 1-800-235-5700

Photography by Donna & Ron Kolb — Exposures Unlimited
The photographed home may have been modified to suit individual tastes.

Charming Brick Ranch

Price Code: C

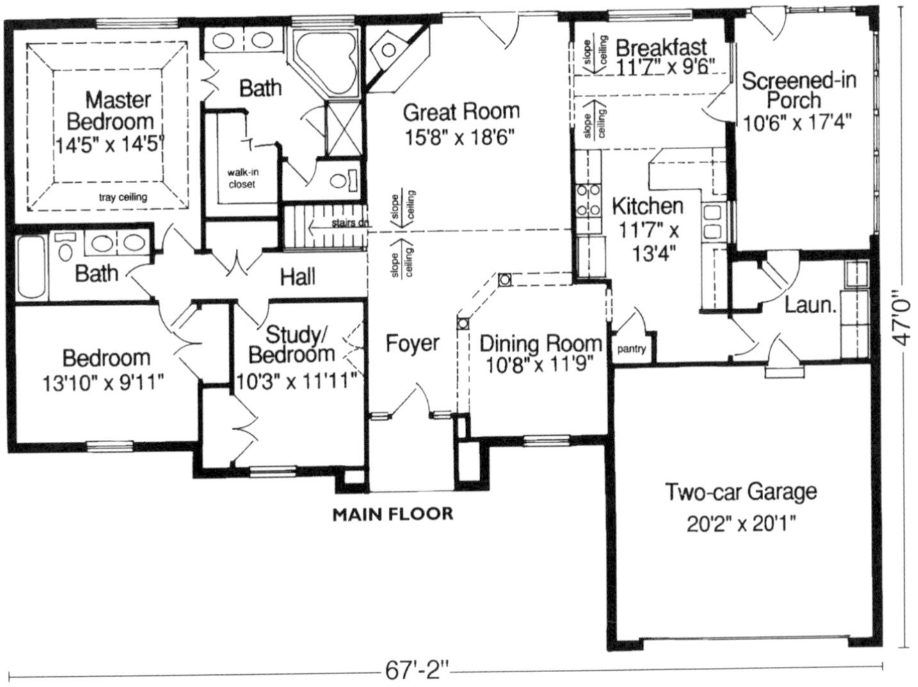

- This plan features:
- — Three bedrooms
- — Two full baths
- Sheltered entrance leads into an open Foyer and Dining Room defined by columns
- Sloped ceiling spans Foyer and Great Room which has corner fireplace and Atrium door to rear yard
- Luxurious Master Bedroom offers tray ceiling and French doors to Bath
- This home is designed with a basement foundation

MAIN FLOOR —1,782 SQ. FT.
GARAGE — 407 SQ. FT.
BASEMENT — 1,735 SQ. FT.

TOTAL LIVING AREA:
1,782 SQ. FT.

Floor plan labels:

Master Bedroom 14'5" x 14'5"
tray ceiling

Bath
walk-in closet

Bath

Bedroom 13'10" x 9'11"

Study/ Bedroom 10'3" x 11'11"

Hall

stairs dn.

slope ceiling

Great Room 15'8" x 18'6"

Breakfast 11'7" x 9'6"

Screened-in Porch 10'6" x 17'4"

Kitchen 11'7" x 13'4"

Laun.

Foyer

Dining Room 10'8" x 11'9"

pantry

Two-car Garage 20'2" x 20'1"

MAIN FLOOR

67'-2"

47'0"

Three Porches
Price Code: C

■ This plan features:
— Three bedrooms
— Two full baths
■ Bedrooms fill the right wing of the home, forming their own private core
■ The Master Bedroom enjoys a private gateway to its own Patio
■ Columns elegantly separate the Great Room and the Dining Area
■ The Kitchen featuring an eating bar for casual dining, opens up to the Dining Area
■ Optional bookshelves in a secondary Bedroom and a computer center in the Dining Area add practicality to beauty
■ A separate Storage Area off the Garage provides plenty of extra room for just about anything
■ This home is designed with crawlspace and slab foundation options

MAIN FLOOR — 1,601 SQ. FT.
GARAGE — 771 SQ. FT.

TOTAL LIVING AREA:
1,601 SQ. FT.

WIDTH 39'-0"
DEPTH 77'-2"

MAIN FLOOR

Country Convenience
Price Code: A

■ This plan features:
—Three bedrooms
—Two full baths
■ A cozy front Porch enhances the curb appeal of this home
■ The Kitchen/Dining Area is crowned by a vaulted ceiling
■ A covered walk connects the Kitchen to the two-car Garage
■ An optional Master Bath includes a soaking tub
■ This home is designed with slab and crawlspace foundation options

MAIN FLOOR — 1,475 SQ. FT.
GARAGE — 455 SQ. FT.

TOTAL LIVING AREA:
1,475 SQ. FT.

WIDTH 43'-0"
DEPTH 43'-0"

MASTER BATH OPTION

MAIN FLOOR

To order your Blueprints, call 1-800-235-5700

Living Room Bay

Price Code: D

- This plan features:
  — Three bedrooms
  — Two full and one half baths
- Floor length windows in the formal Dining Room and Living Room help illuminate the wide Foyer
- The Master Suite has a tray ceiling and a luxury Bath with separate vanities and walk-in closets
- This home is designed with basement and crawlspace foundation options

MAIN FLOOR — 2,201 SQ. FT.
GARAGE — 452 SQ. FT.
BASEMENT — 2,201 SQ. FT.

TOTAL LIVING AREA: 2,201 SQ. FT.

WIDTH 59'-6"
DEPTH 62'-0"

MAIN FLOOR

© Frank Betz Associates, Inc.

BASEMENT STAIR LOCATION OPTION

Compact Traditional for Easy Living

Price Code: C

- This plan features:
  — Three bedrooms
  — Two full baths
- Foyer opens to Living and Dining Rooms defined by a half wall
- Convenient Kitchen has a serving counter for Breakfast Area, Family Room, and Dining Room
- Master Bedroom offers a walk-in closet and private Bath
- Two front Bedrooms with ample closets, share a full hall Bath
- Laundry Room is located for convenience, serving as a sound buffer for the Bedroom wing
- This home is designed with a basement, slab, and crawlspace foundation options

MAIN FLOOR — 1,786 SQ. FT.
PORCH — 223 SQ. FT.
BASEMENT — 1,775 SQ. FT.
GARAGE — 426 SQ. FT.

TOTAL LIVING AREA: 1,786 SQ. FT.

BASEMENT OPTION

MAIN FLOOR

PLAN NO. 97228

PLAN NO. 34976

Family Room at Heart of Home

Price Code: F

■ This plan features:

— Four bedrooms

— Three full baths

■ The Dining Room and Living Room are to the right and left of the Foyer

■ The Dining Room, with French doors, opens to the Kitchen

■ The Master Bedroom is equipped with a double-vanity Bath, with two walk-in closets and a linear closet

■ A cozy fireplace and a decorative ceiling highlight the Family Room

■ This home is designed with slab and crawlspace foundation options

MAIN FLOOR — 2,558 SQ. FT.
GARAGE — 549 SQ. FT.

TOTAL LIVING AREA:
2,558 SQ. FT.

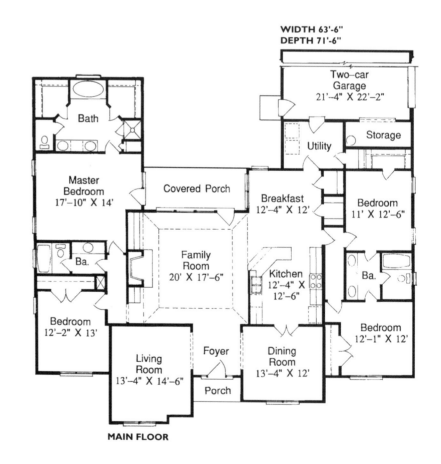

WIDTH 63'-6"
DEPTH 71'-6"

Two-car Garage 21'-4" X 22'-2"

Storage

Utility

Bath

Master Bedroom 17'-10" X 14'

Covered Porch

Breakfast 12'-4" X 12'

Bedroom 11' X 12'-6"

Ba.

Family Room 20' X 17'-6"

Kitchen 12'-4" X 12'-6"

Ba.

Bedroom 12'-2" X 13'

Living Room 13'-4" X 14'-6"

Foyer

Dining Room 13'-4" X 12'

Bedroom 12'-1" X 12'

Porch

MAIN FLOOR

To order your Blueprints, call 1-800-235-5700

Bow Window Adds to Curb Appeal

Price Code: A

- This plan features:
- — Three bedrooms
- — Two full baths
- Curb appeal enhanced by a beautiful bow window in the Living Room and by the front Porch
- A Dining Room that is separated from the Kitchen by only a peninsula counter/eating bar
- More than ample counter space, a double sink, and a Laundry Center in the Kitchen
- A Master Bedroom with a private full Bath and twin closets
- This home is designed with basement, slab, and crawlspace foundation options

MAIN FLOOR — 1,373 SQ. FT.
GARAGE — 400 SQ. FT.

TOTAL LIVING AREA:
1,373 SQ. FT.

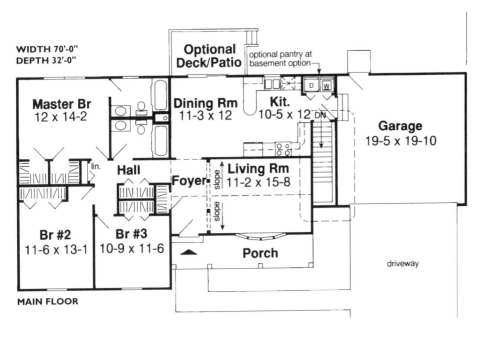

WIDTH 70'-0"
DEPTH 32'-0"

Optional Deck/Patio

optional pantry at basement option

Master Br
12 x 14-2

Dining Rm
11-3 x 12

Kit.
10-5 x 12

D W

DN

Garage
19-5 x 19-10

lin.

Hall

Foyer

slope

slope

Living Rm
11-2 x 15-8

Br #2
11-6 x 13-1

Br #3
10-9 x 11-6

Porch

driveway

MAIN FLOOR

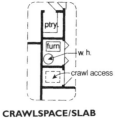

ptry.

furn

w. h.

crawl access

CRAWLSPACE/SLAB OPTION

Brick Magnificence

Price Code: G

■ This plan features:

— Four bedrooms

— Three full baths

■ Large windows and brick detailing using segmented arches give fantastic curb appeal

■ Convenient Ranch layout allows for step-saving, one-floor ease

■ A fireplace in the Living Room adds a warm ambience

■ The Family Room has a second fireplace

■ This home is designed with a slab foundation

MAIN FLOOR — 2,858 SQ. FT.
GARAGE — 768 SQ. FT.

TOTAL LIVING AREA:
2,858 SQ. FT.

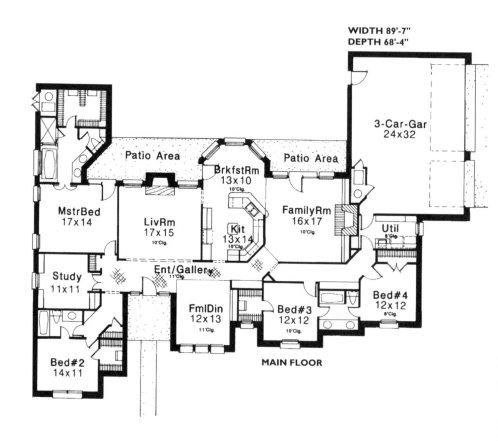

WIDTH 89'-7"
DEPTH 68'-4"

3-Car-Gar
24x32

Patio Area

BrkfstRm
13x10
10'Clg.

Patio Area

MstrBed
17x14

LivRm
17x15
10'Clg.

Kit
13x14
10'Clg.

FamilyRm
16x17
10'Clg.

Util
8'Clg.

Study
11x11

Ent/Gallery
11'Clg.

FmlDin
12x13
11'Clg.

Bed#3
12x12
10'Clg.

Bed#4
12x12
8'Clg.

Bed#2
14x11

MAIN FLOOR

Stone and Stucco Facade

Price Code: G

■ This plan features:
— Three bedrooms
— Two full baths

■ Three different ceiling treatments define the open Foyer, Living, and Dining Rooms

■ An angled island, with sink and dishwasher, separate the Kitchen from the Family Room

■ A tray ceiling, five-piece Bath, and walk-in closet highlight the Master Suite

■ This home is designed with a crawlspace foundation

■ Alternate foundation options available at an additional charge. Please call 1-800-235-5700 for more information.

MAIN FLOOR — 1,848 SQ. FT.

TOTAL LIVING AREA:
1,848 SQ. FT.

MAIN FLOOR

Mix of Stucco and Brick

Price Code: C

■ This plan features:
— Three bedrooms
— Two full baths

■ In this home, 10-foot-high ceilings top most of the living and sleeping areas

■ Ceilings slope at the edges of the Dining Room, the Living Room, and the Master Suite

■ The Garage includes two Storage Areas, one with access from the inside and the other from the backyard

■ This home is designed with slab and crawlspace foundation options

MAIN FLOOR — 1,890 SQ. FT.
GARAGE — 565 SQ. FT.

TOTAL LIVING AREA:
1,890 SQ. FT.

WIDTH 65'-10"
DEPTH 53'-5"

MAIN FLOOR

To order your Blueprints, call 1-800-235-5700

A Collection of Gables

Price Code: L

- This plan features:
  — Four bedrooms
  — Three full and one half baths
- The offset Great Room provides interesting views of the house and site
- Most of one wing is devoted to the Master Suite
- Classic country-European lines make the exterior a crowd pleaser
- This home is designed with a slab foundation

MAIN FLOOR — 2,684 SQ. FT.
GARAGE — 638 SQ. FT.

TOTAL LIVING AREA:
2,684 SQ. FT.

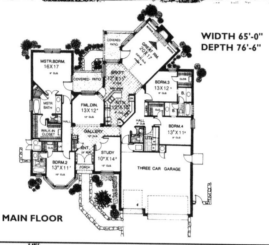

WIDTH 65'-0"
DEPTH 76'-6"

MAIN FLOOR

Cabin in the Woods

Price Code: A

- This plan features:
  — Two bedrooms
  — One full bath
- The large Deck has a wood storage bin
- The Living Room is warmed by a wood stove
- The Kitchen is open to the Living Room and is fully appointed
- Two large Bedrooms each have ample closet space
- A full Bath completes this rustic cabin retreat
- This home is designed with slab and crawlspace foundation options

MAIN FLOOR — 728 SQ. FT.

TOTAL LIVING AREA:
728 SQ. FT.

WIDTH 26'-0"
DEPTH 28'-0"

MAIN FLOOR

To order your Blueprints, call 1-800-235-5700

Designed with the Family in Mind

Price Code: C

■ This plan features:

— Three bedrooms

— Two full and one half baths

■ The Garage leads through the Mud Room and Laundry

■ Bay windows grace the Breakfast Nook and formal Dining Room

■ Behind the Master Bath's whirlpool tub is a shelf for plants

■ A corner fireplace warms the large Great Room

■ Efficiency is a hallmark of the well-designed Kitchen

■ This home is designed with slab and crawlspace foundation options

MAIN FLOOR — 1,954 SQ. FT.
GARAGE — 411 SQ. FT.

TOTAL LIVING AREA:
1,954 SQ. FT

MAIN FLOOR

PATIO
42'-6"x12'-0"

STORAGE
HW
LNDRY/MUD ROOM
16'-11"x8'-5"
MECH
F
W   D

BREAKFAST
11'-7"x11'-2"

F.P.

MASTER BATH
PLANTS
JACC.
SHWR
W.I.C.

GREAT ROOM
13'-0"x29'-5"
(VAULTED)

MASTER BEDROOM
15'-0"x13'-1"
(VAULTED)

KITCHEN
11'-7"x11'-0"
FRIG.

BATH

GARAGE
20'-8"x20'-8"

LINEN

BEDROOM #2
11'-0"x12'-0"
W.I.C.

BEDROOM #3
11'-7"x10'-6"

FORMAL DINING
11'-7"x12'-1"

OPTIONAL HALF-WALL

W.I.C.

WIDTH 74'-6"
DEPTH 43'-0"

COVERED PORCH
32'-6"x10'-0"

Ten-Foot Entry

Price Code: B

- This plan features:
- —Three bedrooms
- —Two full baths
- Large volume Great Room is highlighted by a fireplace
- Decorative ceiling treatment giving elegance to the Dining Room
- Fully-equipped Kitchen with a desk and a Pantry
- Roomy Master Bedroom has a Bath and a large walk-in closet
- This home is designed with a basement foundation
- Alternate foundation options available at an additional charge. Please call 1-800-235-5700 for more information.

MAIN FLOOR — 1,604 SQ. FT.
GARAGE — 466 SQ. FT.

TOTAL LIVING AREA:
1,604 SQ. FT.

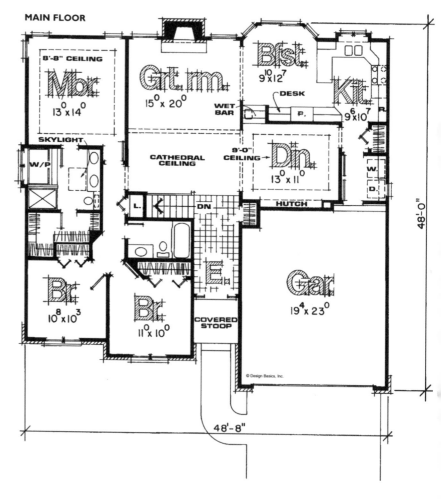

MAIN FLOOR

To order your Blueprints, call 1-800-235-5700

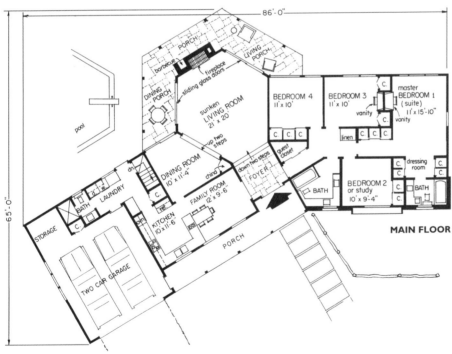

MAIN FLOOR

Western Ranch House

Price Code: C

■ This plan features:

— Four bedrooms

— Three full baths

■ Authentic Ranch styling with long Loggia, posts and braces, hand-split shake roof and cross-buck doors

■ A Texas-sized hexagonal, sunken Living Room with two solid walls, one with a fireplace

■ A Porch surrounding the Living Room on three sides

■ A Master Suite with a private Master Bath

■ This home is designed with a basement foundation

MAIN FLOOR — 1,830 SQ. FT.
BASEMENT — 1,830 SQ. FT.
GARAGE — 540 SQ. FT.

TOTAL LIVING AREA:
1,830 SQ. FT.

Photography by Donna & Ron Kolb — Exposures Unlimited
The photographed home may have been modified to suit individual tastes.

Simple Lines Enhanced by Elegant Window Treatment

Price Code: A

■ This plan features:

— Three bedrooms

— Two full baths

■ A huge arched window that floods the front room with natural light

■ A homey, well-lit Office or Den

■ A Living Room with a sloped ceiling, a fireplace, and a window wall

■ A Master Bedroom sporting a private Bath with a roomy walk-in closet and a whirlpool tub

■ This home is designed with basement, slab, and crawlspace foundation options

MAIN FLOOR — 1,492 SQ. FT.
BASEMENT — 1,486 SQ. FT.
GARAGE — 462 SQ. FT.

TOTAL LIVING AREA:
1,492 SQ. FT.

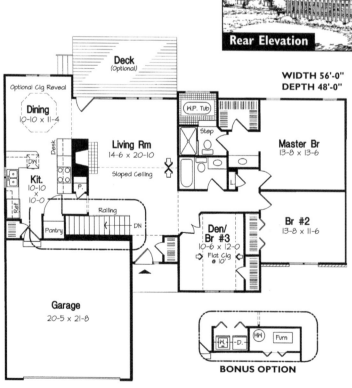

Rear Elevation

WIDTH 56'-0"
DEPTH 48'-0"

MAIN FLOOR

BONUS OPTION

To order your Blueprints, call 1-800-235-5700

One-Story Country Home

Price Code: A

- This plan features:
  — Three bedrooms
  — Two full baths
- A Living Room has a high ceiling and a heat-circulating fireplace
- An efficient Kitchen accesses the Dining Room and rear Terrace
- A Dinette Area for informal eating in the Kitchen can comfortably seat six people
- A Master Suite is arranged with a large Dressing Area
- This home is designed with basement and slab foundation options

MAIN FLOOR — 1,367 SQ. FT.
BASEMENT — 1,267 SQ. FT.
GARAGE — 431 SQ. FT.

TOTAL LIVING AREA:
1,367 SQ. FT.

WIDTH 71'-4"
DEPTH 33'-10"

whirlpool tub 5'-6"

glass blocks

M.B.R.

16-6 x 15-2 AVE.

DRESSING

W.I.C.

B. R.
11-0 x 12-0
high ceiling

B. R.
10-6 x 10-0

TERR.

heat-circul. f.p.

L. R.
13-0 x 20-6
high ceiling

skylight above

KIT.
14-8 x 12-4

DINETTE

sl. gl. dr.

dw

ref.

w. d.

D. R.
11-4 x 10-0

TWO CAR GAR.
21-0 x 19-6

STOR.

P.

columns

railing

MAIN FLOOR

Central Courtyard Features Pool

Price Code: D

■ This plan features:

— Three bedrooms

— One full bath and one three-quarter baths

■ A central Courtyard complete with a Pool

■ A secluded Master Bedroom accented by a skylight, spacious walk-in closet, and private Bath

■ An efficient Kitchen easily serving the Patio for convenient outdoor entertaining

■ A detached two-car Garage

■ This home is designed with a crawlspace foundation

MAIN FLOOR — 2,194 SQ. FT.
GARAGE — 576 SQ. FT.

*TOTAL LIVING AREA:
2,194 SQ. FT.*

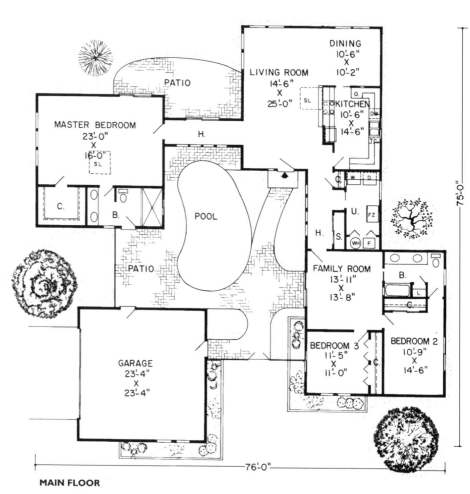

MAIN FLOOR

To order your Blueprints, call 1-800-235-5700

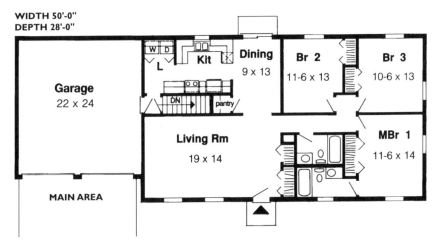

Rear Elevation

Ranch Provides Great Kitchen Area

Price Code: A

■ This plan features:

— Three bedrooms

— Two full baths

■ A Dining Room with sliding glass doors to the backyard

■ Access to the Garage through the Laundry Room

■ A Master Bedroom with a private full Bath

■ A two-car Garage

■ This home is designed with basement, slab, and crawlspace foundation options

MAIN FLOOR — 1,400 SQ. FT.
BASEMENT — 1,400 SQ. FT.
GARAGE — 528 SQ. FT.

TOTAL LIVING AREA: 1,400 SQ. FT.

WIDTH 50'-0"
DEPTH 28'-0"

Garage 22 x 24

MAIN AREA

W D
L
Kit

Dining 9 x 13

Br 2 11-6 x 13

Br 3 10-6 x 13

DN pantry

Living Rm 19 x 14

MBr 1 11-6 x 14

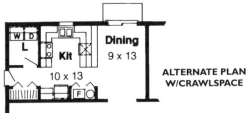

W D
L
Kit 10 x 13

Dining 9 x 13

F

ALTERNATE PLAN W/CRAWLSPACE

Easy One-Floor Living

Price Code: B

- This plan features:
— Three bedrooms
— Two full baths

- A spacious Family Room topped by a vaulted ceiling and highlighted by a large fireplace and a French door to the rear yard

- A Pantry and a peninsula counter which adds more efficiency to the Kitchen

- A vaulted ceiling over the cozy Sitting Room in the Master Suite

- This home is designed with basement, slab, and crawlspace foundation options

MAIN FLOOR — 1,671 SQ. FT.
BASEMENT — 1,685 SQ. FT.
GARAGE — 400 SQ. FT.

TOTAL LIVING AREA:
1,671 SQ. FT.

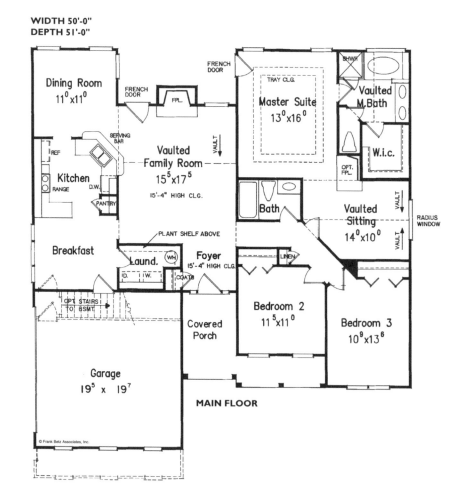

WIDTH 50'-0"
DEPTH 51'-0"

Dining Room 11⁰x11⁰

FRENCH DOOR

FRENCH DOOR

TRAY CLG.

Master Suite 13⁰x16⁰

SHWR

Vaulted M.Bath

SERVING BAR

REF

Kitchen
RANGE   D.W.

PANTRY

Vaulted Family Room 15⁵x17⁵

15'-4" HIGH CLG.

VAULT

OPT. FPL.

W.i.c.

FPL.

PLANT SHELF ABOVE

Bath

Vaulted Sitting 14⁰x10⁰

RADIUS WINDOW

Breakfast

Laund.
D.   W.

WH

Foyer 15'-4" HIGH CLG.

LINEN

COATS

OPT STAIRS TO BSMT.

Covered Porch

Bedroom 2 11⁵x11⁰

Bedroom 3 10⁹x13⁶

Garage 19⁵ x 19⁷

MAIN FLOOR

© Frank Betz Associates, Inc.

To order your Blueprints, call 1-800-235-5700

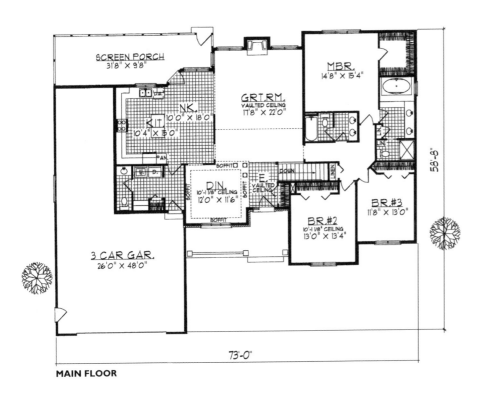

SCREEN PORCH
31'8" X 9'8"

MBR.
14'8" X 15'4"

GRT.RM.
VAULTED CEILING
17'8" X 22'0"

NK.
10'0" X 18'0"

KIT.
10'4" X 15'0"

PAN.

SOFFIT

DIN
10'1 1/8" CEILING
12'0" X 11'6"

E.
VAULTED
CEILING

DOWN

LINEN

LIN
LIN

BOFFIT

B.R.#3
11'8" X 13'0"

B.R.#2
10'4 1/8" CEILING
13'0" X 13'4"

3 CAR GAR.
26'0" X 48'0"

58'-8"

73'-0"

MAIN FLOOR

Luxury on One Level
Price Code: D

■ This plan features:

— Three bedrooms

— Two full and one half baths

■ Covered front Porch leads into Entry and Great Room with vaulted ceiling

■ Arched soffits and columns impact the formal Dining Room

■ Country-sized Kitchen with a Pantry, work island, eating Nook with Screen Porch beyond, and nearby Laundry/Garage Entry

■ Master Bedroom offers a walk-in closet and a luxurious Bath

■ This home is designed with a basement foundation

MAIN FLOOR — 2,196 SQ. FT.
BASEMENT — 2,196 SQ. FT.

TOTAL LIVING AREA:
2,196 SQ. FT.

Country Charmer

Price Code: A

- This plan features:
- —Three bedrooms
- —Two full baths
- Quaint front Porch is perfect for sitting and relaxing
- Great Room opening into Dining Area and Kitchen
- Master Suite with a private Bath, walk-in closet, and built-in shelves
- Two large secondary Bedrooms in the front of the home share a hall Bath
- Two-car Garage located in the rear of the home
- This home is designed with slab and crawlspace foundation options

MAIN FLOOR — 1,438 SQ. FT.
GARAGE —   486 SQ. FT.

TOTAL LIVING AREA:
1,438 SQ. FT.

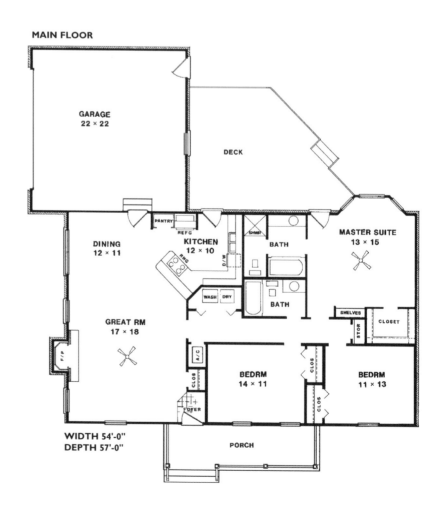

MAIN FLOOR

GARAGE
22 × 22

DECK

MASTER SUITE
13 × 15

PANTRY
REFG
DINING
12 × 11
KITCHEN
12 × 10
BATH

SHELVES
STOR
CLOSET
WASH DRY
BATH

GREAT RM
17 × 18

F/P

A/C
BEDRM
14 × 11
CLOS

BEDRM
11 × 13

CLOS
CLOS
CLOS

FOYER

WIDTH 54'-0"
DEPTH 57'-0"
PORCH

To order your Blueprints, call 1-800-235-5700

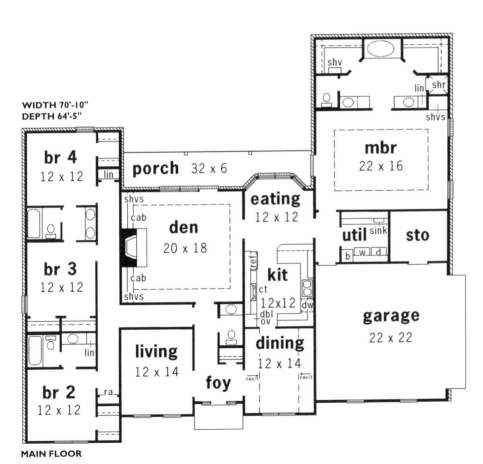

WIDTH 70'-10"
DEPTH 64'-5"

br 4 12 x 12 | lin

porch 32 x 6

shvs / cab

den 20 x 18

cab / shvs

eating 12 x 12

ref

kit 12 x 12
ct / dbl / ov / dw

mbr 22 x 16

util sink
b / w / d

sto

br 3 12 x 12

br 2 12 x 12 | ra

living 12 x 14

foy
vault

dining 12 x 14
vault

garage 22 x 22

shv

lin / shr

shvs

MAIN FLOOR

European Style

Price Code: F

■ This plan features:

— Four bedrooms

— Three full and one half baths

■ Central Foyer between spacious Living and Dining Rooms

■ Hub Kitchen with extended counter and nearby Utility/ Garage Entry

■ Spacious Den with a hearth fireplace between built-ins

■ Master Bedroom wing with decorative ceiling and plush Bath with two walk-in closets

■ Three additional Bedrooms with ample closets and full Baths

■ This home is designed with slab and crawlspace foundation options

MAIN FLOOR — 2,727 SQ. FT.
GARAGE — 569 SQ. FT.

TOTAL LIVING AREA:
2,727 SQ. FT.

Brick Home with Four Bedrooms

Price Code: D

■ This plan features:

— Four bedrooms

— Two full and one three-quarter baths

■ Four roomy Bedrooms, including the Master Bedroom

■ A centrally-located Family Room including a fireplace, wetbar, and access to the Patio

■ A large Dining Room at the front of the home for entertaining

■ An interesting-shaped Kitchen and Nook with an adjoining Utility Room

■ This home is designed with a slab foundation

MAIN FLOOR — 2,070 SQ. FT.
GARAGE — 474 SQ. FT.

TOTAL LIVING AREA:
2,070 SQ. FT.

WIDTH 52'-0"
DEPTH 68'-6"

Rear Elevation

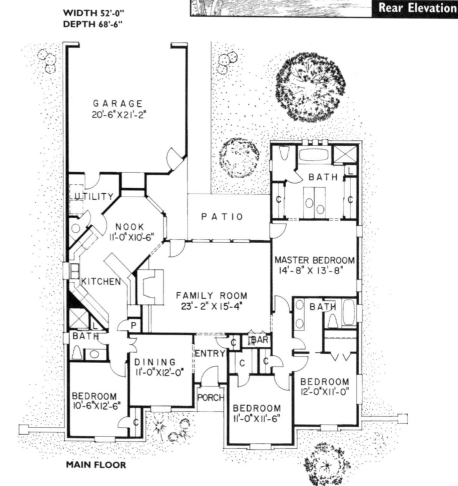

MAIN FLOOR

GARAGE
20'-6" X 21'-2"

UTILITY

PATIO

NOOK
11'-0" X 10'-6"

KITCHEN

BATH

DINING
11'-0" X 12'-0"

ENTRY

BAR

BEDROOM
10'-6" X 12'-6"

PORCH

BEDROOM
11'-0" X 11'-6"

FAMILY ROOM
23'-2" X 15'-4"

MASTER BEDROOM
14'-8" X 13'-8"

BATH

BATH

BEDROOM
12'-0" X 11'-0"

To order your Blueprints, call 1-800-235-5700

Carefree Convenience

Price Code: B

- This plan features:
— Three bedrooms
— Two full baths
- A galley Kitchen centrally located between the Dining, Breakfast, and Living Room areas
- A Master Suite with two closets and a double-vanity Bath
- Two additional Bedrooms sharing a full hall Bath
- This home is designed with a slab foundation

MAIN FLOOR — 1,600 SQ. FT.
GARAGE — 465 SQ. FT.

TOTAL LIVING AREA:
1,600 SQ. FT.

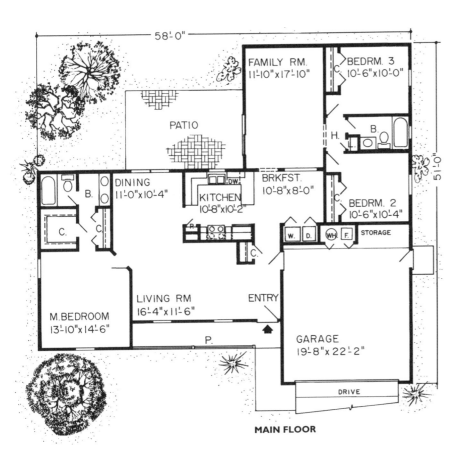

MAIN FLOOR

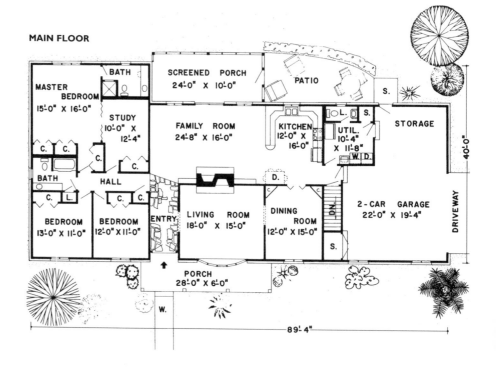

Rear Elevation

Home Reminiscent of the South

Price Code: E

■ This plan features:

— Three bedrooms

— One full and one half baths

■ A Master Bedroom Suite with access to a Study

■ Fireplaces enhancing the formal Living Room and spacious Family Room

■ A lovely, Screened Porch/Patio skirting the Family Room and the Kitchen

■ A Utility Room with access into the Storage and Garage areas

■ This home is designed with a basement foundation

MAIN FLOOR — 2,466 SQ. FT.
BASEMENT — 1,447 SQ. FT.
GARAGE — 664 SQ. FT.

TOTAL LIVING AREA:
2,466 SQ. FT.

MAIN FLOOR

Gabled Roofline

Price Code: G

■ This plan features:
— Four bedrooms
— Two full and one three-quarter baths
■ The U-shaped Kitchen enjoys a center island and a service bar that opens to the Breakfast Nook
■ The bonus space above the three-car Garage offers an ideal location for a Grandparents' Suite
■ This home is designed with a slab foundation

MAIN FLOOR — 2,755 SQ. FT.
BONUS — 440 SQ. FT.
GARAGE — 724 SQ. FT.

TOTAL LIVING AREA:
2,755 SQ. FT.

WIDTH 73'-0"
DEPTH 82'-8"

MAIN FLOOR

BONUS

Country Charm

Price Code: A

■ This plan features:
— Three bedrooms
— Two full and one half baths
■ 10-foot-high ceilings in the Living Room, Family Room and Dinette Area
■ A heat-circulating fireplace
■ A Master Bath with stall shower and whirlpool tub
■ A two-car Garage with access through the Mudroom
■ This home is designed with a basement foundation

MAIN FLOOR — 1,203 SQ. FT.
LOWER FLOOR — 676 SQ. FT.
GARAGE — 509 SQ. FT.

TOTAL LIVING AREA:
1,203 SQ. FT.

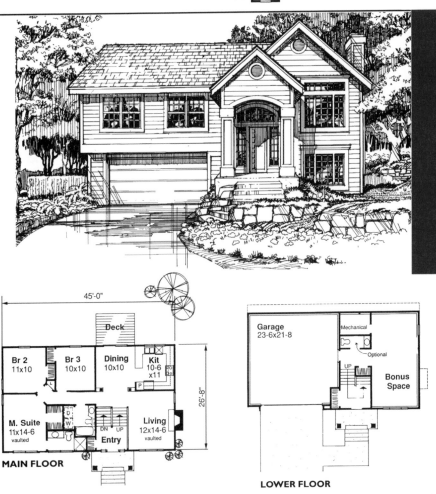

MAIN FLOOR

LOWER FLOOR

Easy Entertaining

Price Code: G

- This plan features:
— Three bedrooms
— Two full baths
- Formal and informal entertaining areas have easy access to the wetbar
- The open Foyer and Dining Room share views to the rear yard through the Atrium door in the Living Room
- Built-in features include an entertainment center in the Family Room and a desk in the Kitchen
- This home is designed with a slab foundation
- Alternate foundation options available at an additional charge. Please call 1-800-235-5700 for more information.

MAIN FLOOR — 1,848 SQ. FT.
GARAGE — 571 SQ. FT.

TOTAL LIVING AREA:
1,848 SQ. FT.

Bedroom 1
10'-4" x 12'-0"
8'-0" Flat Clg.

Bath 2

Nook
8'-8" x 8'-8"
Vaulted Clg.

Porch
25'-4" x 10'-0"

ent. center

Family Room
12'-4" x 17'-4"
Vaulted Clg.

desk

Bedroom 2
10'-4" x 12'-0"
8'-0" Flat Clg.

Kitchen
8'-8" x 14'-6"
Vaulted Clg.

Living Room
13'-0" x 15'-0"
Stepped Clg.

Master Suite
11'-8" x 15'-0"
Tray Clg.

L.T.

A/C D W

wet bar

Utility
6'-8" x 6'-8"

Dining Room
11'-8" x 11'-0"
Tray Clg.

Foyer
Vaulted Clg.

WIC M. Bath

Garage
22'-8" x 22'-4"

Porch
26'-8" x 8'-0"

WIDTH 58'-0"
DEPTH 59'-6"

© Sater Design Collection

MAIN FLOOR

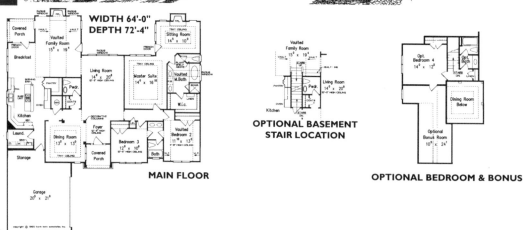

Unfinished Bonus Area

Price Code: E

- This plan features:
— Three bedrooms
— Two full and one half baths
- A walk-in Pantry and long island with cooktop highlight the Kitchen
- Radius windows adorn each side of the fireplace in the Family Room
- This home is designed with basement and crawlspace foundation options

MAIN FLOOR — 2,491 SQ. FT.
BONUS — 588 SQ. FT.
GARAGE — 522 SQ. FT.

TOTAL LIVING AREA:
2,491 SQ. FT

WIDTH 64'-0"
DEPTH 72'-4"

Covered Porch

Vaulted Family Room
15' x 19'

Sitting Room
14' x 10'

Breakfast

Living Room
14' x 20'

Master Suite
14' x 16'

Vaulted M. Bath

Pantry

Kitchen

W.i.c.

Dining Room
13' x 13'

Foyer

Bedroom 3
12' x 10'

Vaulted Bedroom 2
11'-10" x 13'-6"

Covered Porch

Bath

Laund.

Storage

Garage
20' x 21'

MAIN FLOOR

Vaulted Family Room
15' x 19'

Pantry

Kitchen

Living Room
14' x 20'

OPTIONAL BASEMENT STAIR LOCATION

Opt. Bedroom 4
14' x 12'

Opt. Bath

Dining Room Below

Optional Bonus Room
10'-5" x 24'

OPTIONAL BEDROOM & BONUS

To order your Blueprints, call 1-800-235-5700

Photography supplied by Larry E. Belk

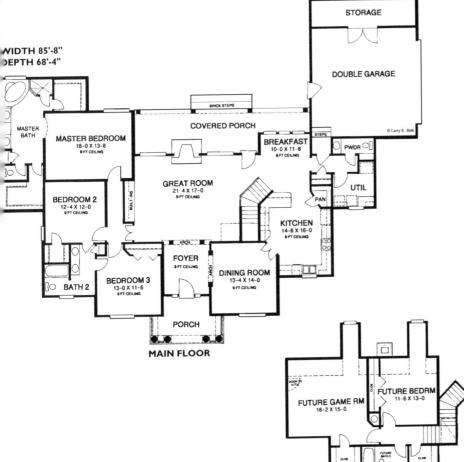

WIDTH 85'-8"
DEPTH 68'-4"

STORAGE

DOUBLE GARAGE

BRICK STEPS

COVERED PORCH

© Larry E. Belk

MASTER
BATH

MASTER BEDROOM
18-0 X 13-6
9 FT CEILING

STEPS

BREAKFAST
10-0 X 11-6
9 FT CEILING

PWDR

BUILT-INS

GREAT ROOM
21-4 X 17-0
9 FT CEILING

UTIL

PAN

BEDROOM 2
12-4 X 12-0
9 FT CEILING

KITCHEN
14-6 X 16-0
9 FT CEILING

ARCH

FOYER
9 FT CEILING

ARCH

BATH 2

BEDROOM 3
13-0 X 11-6
9 FT CEILING

DINING ROOM
13-4 X 14-0
9 FT CEILING

PORCH

MAIN FLOOR

DOOR TO
ATTIC

FUTURE GAME RM
16-2 X 15-0

CLO

FUTURE BEDRM
11-6 X 13-0

FUTURE
BATH 3

CLO

CLO

BONUS

Stately Elegance
Price Code: E

■ This plan features:

— Three bedrooms

— Two full and one half baths

■ Elegant columns frame Entry into Foyer and expansive Great Room beyond

■ Efficient Kitchen ideal for busy cook with walk-in Pantry, Breakfast Area, and access to formal Dining Room, Utility Room, and Garage

■ A private Master Bedroom Suite boasts a Bath with two walk-in closets and whirlpool tub

■ This home is designed with slab and crawlspace foundation options

MAIN FLOOR — 2,409 SQ. FT.
BONUS ROOM — 709 SQ. FT.
GARAGE — 644 SQ. FT.

TOTAL LIVING AREA:
2,409 SQ. FT.

Distinctive Ranch

Price Code: C

■ This plan features:

— Three bedrooms

— Two full baths

■ This hipped-roofed Ranch has an exterior that mixes brick and siding

■ The Great Room has a cathedral ceiling and a rear-wall fireplace

■ The Dining Room features a high ceiling and a bright front window

■ The two-car Garage could easily be expanded to fit three with a door placed in the rear Storage Area

■ This home is designed with a basement foundation

MAIN FLOOR — 1,802 SQ. FT.
BASEMENT — 1,802 SQ. FT.

TOTAL LIVING AREA:
1,802 SQ. FT.

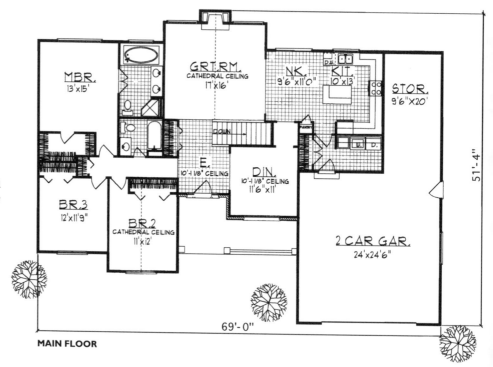

MAIN FLOOR

MBR.
13'x15'

GRT. RM.
CATHEDRAL CEILING
17'x16'

NK.
9'6"x11'0"

KIT.
10'x13'

STOR.
9'6"x20'

DOWN

PANTRY

E.
10'-1 1/8" CEILING

DIN.
10'-1 1/8" CEILING
11'6"x11'

BR. 3
12'x11'9"

BR. 2
CATHEDRAL CEILING
11'x12'

2 CAR GAR.
24'x24'6"

51'-4"

69'-0"

To order your Blueprints, call 1-800-235-5700

Rear Elevation

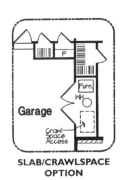

Garage

Crawl Space Access

SLAB/CRAWLSPACE OPTION

Easy Living

Price Code: A

- This plan features:
  — Three bedrooms
  — Two full baths

- A dramatic sloped ceiling and a massive fireplace in the Living Room

- A Dining Room crowned by a sloping ceiling and a plant shelf

- A U-shaped Kitchen with abundant cabinets, a window over the sink, and a walk-in Pantry

- A Master Suite with a private full Bath, decorative ceiling, and walk-in closet

- This home is designed with basement, slab, and crawlspace foundation options

MAIN FLOOR — 1,456 SQ. FT.
BASEMENT — 1,448 SQ. FT.
GARAGE — 452 SQ. FT.

TOTAL LIVING AREA:
1,456 SQ. FT.

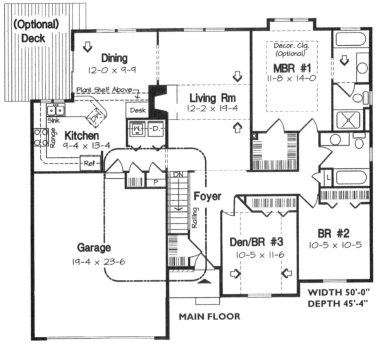

(Optional) Deck

Dining
12-0 x 9-9

Plant Shelf Above

Sink

Kitchen
9-4 x 13-4

Range

Ref

Desk

Living Rm
12-2 x 19-4

Decor. Clg. (Optional)

MBR #1
11-8 x 14-0

W D

DN

P

Foyer

Railing

Garage
19-4 x 23-6

Den/BR #3
10-5 x 11-6

BR #2
10-5 x 10-5

WIDTH 50'-0"
DEPTH 45'-4"

MAIN FLOOR

Formal Balance

Price Code: A

■ This plan features:

— Three bedrooms

— Two full baths

■ A cathedral ceiling in the Living Room with a heat-circulating fireplace as the focal point

■ A bow window in the Dining Room that adds elegance as well as natural light

■ A well-equipped Kitchen that efficiently serves both the Dinette and the formal Dining Room

■ A Master Bedroom with three closets and a private Master Bath with sliding glass doors to the Master Deck with a hot tub

■ This home is designed with basement and slab foundation options

MAIN FLOOR — 1,476 SQ. FT.
BASEMENT — 1,361 SQ. FT.
GARAGE — 548 SQ. FT.

TOTAL LIVING AREA:

1,476 SQ. FT.

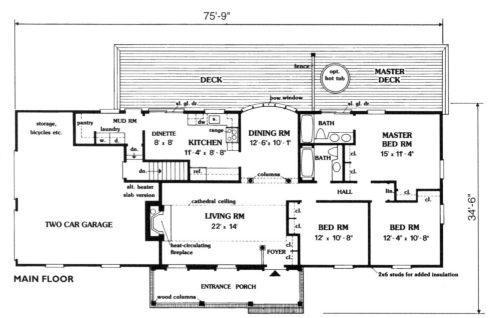

To order your Blueprints, call 1-800-235-5700

MAIN AREA

DECK

SERVING BAR

BREAKFAST

D.W.

DBL. SINK

KITCHEN
10'-0" X 13'-0"

JENN-AIRE RANGE

PANTRY   DESK

COFFERED CLG.
DINING RM.
11'-0" X 11'-6"

CHINA

WOODSTOVE
ALCOVE

VAULTED
FAMILY RM.
19'-4" X 18'-8"

8' HIGH WALL

2/0 X 2/0
SKYLIGHT

MSTR. BDRM.
16'-0" X 13'-4"

GLASS BLOCKS

5/0 WHIRLPOOL
GARDEN TUB

WALK-IN
WARDROBE

M.
BATH

LINEN

SHOWER

VANITY
BATH

5/0 TUB

BDRM. #3
11'-2" X 10'-0"

VLTD.
ENTRY

2/0 x 6/0
SKYLIGHT

VAULTED
STUDY/BDRM. #4
10'-6" X 11'-8"

OPTIONAL
DOOR POSITION

LINEN

LAUNDRY

DRYER WASHER

W/H   EFF-GAS
FURN.

WARDROBE

BDRM. #2
11'-2" X 11'-0"

VAULTED
LIVING RM.
13'-0" X 18'-0"

FIREPLACE

BOOKS   WNDW.   BOOKS
        SEAT

GARAGE
27'-4" X 20'-0"/24'-0"

WIDTH 58'-0"
DEPTH 60'-0"

Four-Bedroom Charmer
Price Code: D

■ This plan features:

— Four bedrooms

— Two full baths

■ A vaulted ceiling in the skylit Entry

■ A Living Room with a masonry fireplace, large windowed bay, and vaulted ceiling

■ A coffered ceiling and built-in china cabinet in the Dining Room

■ An island cooktop and built-in Pantry in the Kitchen

■ A luxurious Master Bedroom with whirlpool garden tub

■ A Study with a window seat and built-in bookshelves

■ This home is designed with a crawlspace foundation

MAIN FLOOR — 2,185 SQ. FT.

TOTAL LIVING AREA:
2,185 SQ. FT.

Symmetrical and Stately

Price Code: E

■ This plan features:

— Four bedrooms

— Two full and one half baths

■ Double-columned Porch leads into the open Foyer

■ Decorative ceiling crowns the Den with a hearth fireplace and built-in shelves

■ Large, efficient Kitchen with a peninsula serving counter, and a Breakfast Area, adjoining the Utility and the Garage

■ Master Bedroom suite has a decorative ceiling and dual vanity

■ This home is designed with slab and crawlspace foundation options

MAIN FLOOR — 2,387 SQ. FT.
GARAGE — 505 SQ. FT.

TOTAL LIVING AREA:
    2,387 SQ. FT.

MAIN FLOOR

MASTER BEDROOM
15'X14'

MASTER BATH

PORCH
19'X8'

GARAGE
21'X22'

BEDROOM 4
12'X11'

DEN
19'X20'

STO

1/2 BATH

UTILITY

BATH 2

BEDROOM 3
12'X12'

BEDROOM 2
11'-6"X12'-6"

FOYER

DINING
14'X12'-6"

KITCHEN
15'X14'

PORCH

BREAKFAST
10'X15'

WIDTH 64'-10"
DEPTH 54'-10"

Country Couture

Price Code: H

- This plan features:
  — Three bedrooms
  — Two full baths
- Deep-cut trim work underscores front Porch detail and plant boxes add a finishing touch
- Coffered ceilings expand the open Living and Dining Rooms
- Built-ins abound throughout and include an entertainment center, art niche, bookshelves, Kitchen desk and corner walk-in Pantry
- The spacious Kitchen has plenty of room in which to work, plus light from the bay-windowed Nook
- This home is designed with basement and slab foundation options
- Alternate foundation options available at an additional charge. Please call 1-800-235-5700 for more information.

MAIN FLOOR — 2,502 SQ. FT.
GARAGE — 612 SQ. FT.
PORCH — 397 SQ. FT.

TOTAL LIVING AREA:
2,502 SQ. FT

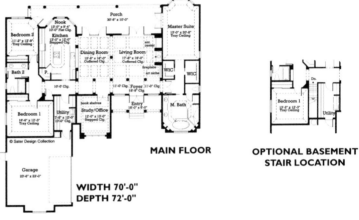

MAIN FLOOR

OPTIONAL BASEMENT
STAIR LOCATION

WIDTH 70'-0"
DEPTH 72'-0"

Charming Distinction

Price Code: G

- This plan features:
  — Three bedrooms
  — Two full baths
- Cathedral ceilings and plant shelves add to the spaciousness inside
- In the Living Room, a flush-hearth fireplace and built-in entertainment center add to your enjoyment
- Columns and abundant natural light accent the formal Dining Room and Breakfast Nook
- This home is designed with a basement foundation
- Alternate foundation options available at an additional charge. Please call 1-800-235-5700 for more information.

MAIN FLOOR — 1,822 SQ. FT.
BASEMENT — 1,822 SQ. FT.
GARAGE — 537 SQ. FT.
PORCH — 287 SQ. FT.

TOTAL LIVING AREA:
1,822 SQ. FT

WIDTH 58'-0"
DEPTH 66'-8"

MAIN FLOOR

A Modern Slant on a Country Theme

Price Code: B

■ This plan features:

—Three bedrooms

—Two full and one half baths

■ Country-styled front Porch highlighting exterior, enhanced by dormer windows

■ Great Room accented by a quaint corner fireplace and a ceiling fan

■ Dining Area adjacent to the Great Room for easy entertaining

■ Kitchen has a convenient snack bar for meals on-the-go

■ Two additional Bedrooms sharing a full hall Bath

■ This home is designed with slab and crawlspace foundation options

MAIN FLOOR — 1,648 SQ. FT.
GARAGE — 479 SQ. FT.

TOTAL LIVING AREA:
1,648 SQ. FT.

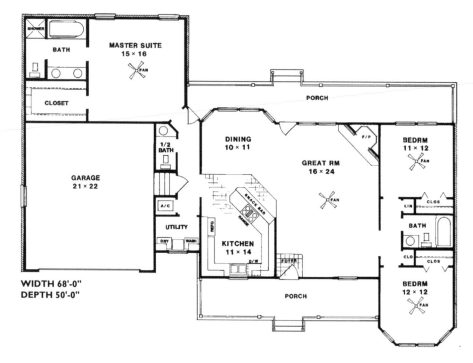

MAIN FLOOR

WIDTH 68'-0"
DEPTH 50'-0"

To order your Blueprints, call 1-800-235-5700

Visual Impact

Price Code: E

- This plan features:
— Four bedrooms
— Two full and one half baths
- Two dormers centered over double arches announce the entrance of this stylish brick and siding one-story
- Classic columns provide visual impact at the front door and a see-through fireplace adds a cozy feel to both the Dining Room and Great Room
- Bedrooms two and three, both with walk-in closets, are located near each other
- Bedroom four is situated for use as either a Bedroom or a Study
- This home is designed with crawlspace and slab foundation options

MAIN FLOOR — 2,389 SQ. FT.
GARAGE — 543 SQ. FT.

TOTAL LIVING AREA: 2,389 SQ. FT.

WIDTH 75'-2"
DEPTH 61'-4"

MAIN FLOOR

© Larry E. Belk

Windows add Warmth to all Living Areas

Price Code: B

- This plan features:
— Three bedrooms
— Two full baths
- A Master Suite with huge double, walk-in closets and private Bath
- A second and third Bedroom with ample closet space
- A Kitchen equipped with an island counter and flowing easily into the Dining and Family Rooms
- A Laundry Room conveniently located near all three Bedrooms
- This home is designed with basement, slab, and crawlspace foundation options

MAIN FLOOR— 1,672 SQ. FT.
GARAGE — 566 SQ. FT.

TOTAL LIVING AREA: 1,672 SQ. FT.

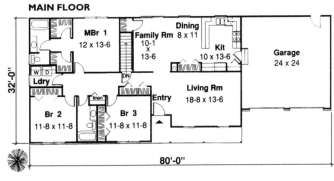

MAIN FLOOR

MBr 1
12 x 13-6

Family Rm
10-1
x
13-6

Dining
8 x 11

Kit
10 x 13-6

Garage
24 x 24

Ldry

W D

Br 2
11-8 x 11-8

linen

Br 3
11-8 x 11-8

DN

Entry

Living Rm
18-8 x 13-6

32'-0"

80'-0"

BONUS OPTION

Family Rm
13-7
x
13-6

Dining
8 x 11

Kit
10 x 13-6

optional wall location

Small yet Lavishly Appointed

Price Code: C

■ This plan features:

— Three bedrooms

— Two full and one half baths

■ The Dining Room, Living Room, Foyer and Master Bath are all topped by high ceilings

■ Master Bedroom features a decorative tray ceiling

■ Family Room has a large fireplace and a French door

■ This home is designed with basement and crawlspace foundation options

MAIN FLOOR — 1,845 SQ. FT.
BONUS — 409 SQ. FT.
BASEMENT — 1,845 SQ. FT.
GARAGE — 529 SQ. FT.

TOTAL LIVING AREA:
1,845 SQ. FT.

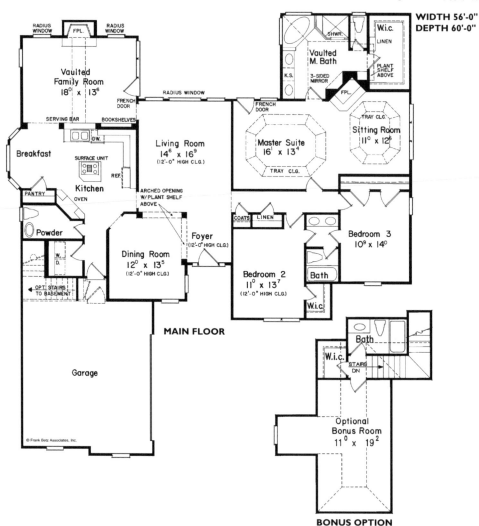

Traditional Ranch Plan

Price Code: D

■ This plan features:

—Three bedrooms

—Two full baths

■ Large Foyer set between the formal Living and Dining Rooms

■ Spacious Great Room adjacent to the open Kitchen /Breakfast Area

■ Secluded Master Suite highlighted by the Master Bath with garden tub, separate shower, and double vanities

■ Bay window allowing bountiful natural light into the Breakfast Area

■ This home is designed with basement and crawlspace foundation options

MAIN FLOOR — 2,218 SQ. FT.
BASEMENT — 1,658 SQ. FT.
GARAGE — 528 SQ. FT.

TOTAL LIVING AREA:
2,218 SQ. FT.

Floor plan labels:

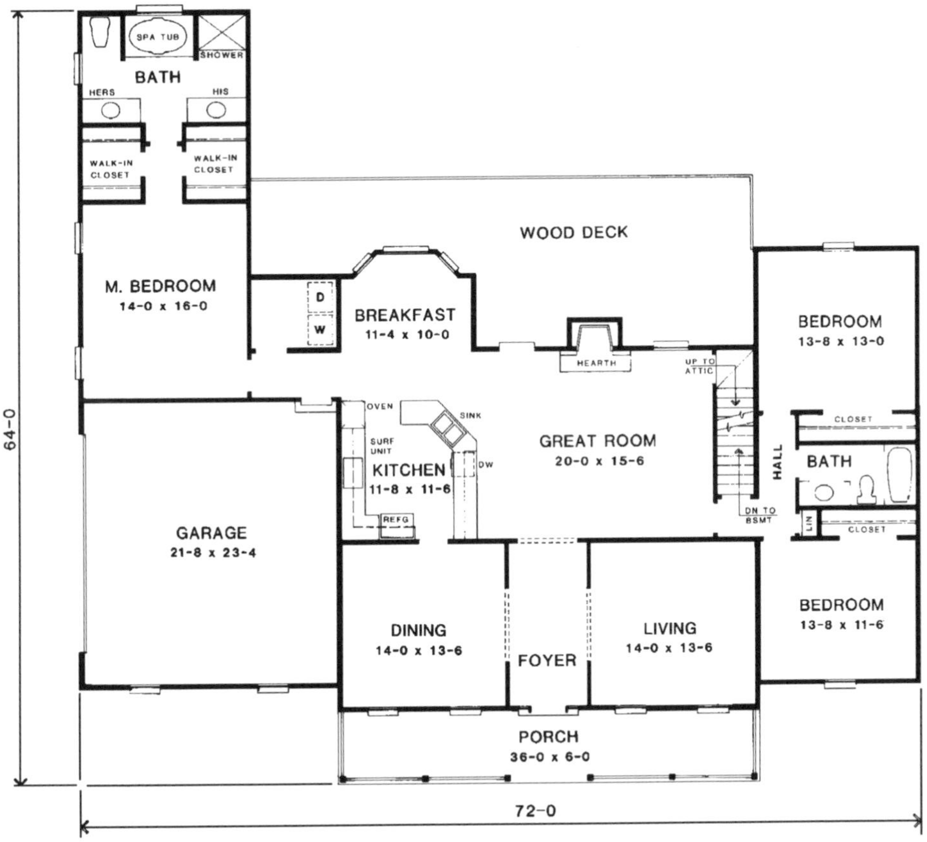

SPA TUB · SHOWER · BATH · HERS · HIS · WALK-IN CLOSET · WALK-IN CLOSET

M. BEDROOM 14-0 x 16-0

D W

BREAKFAST 11-4 x 10-0

WOOD DECK

BEDROOM 13-8 x 13-0

CLOSET

BATH

HEARTH

UP TO ATTIC

OVEN · SURF UNIT · SINK

KITCHEN 11-8 x 11-6

DW

GREAT ROOM 20-0 x 15-6

HALL

REFG

DN TO BSMT

LIN

CLOSET

GARAGE 21-8 x 23-4

BEDROOM 13-8 x 11-6

DINING 14-0 x 13-6

FOYER

LIVING 14-0 x 13-6

PORCH 36-0 x 6-0

64-0

72-0

MAIN FLOOR

To order your Blueprints, call 1-800-235-5700

Divided Three-Car Garage

Price Code: F

■ This plan features:
— Three bedrooms
— Two full and one half baths
■ A Shop Area connects the divided Garage, which provides room for three vehicles
■ The large Great Room is the hub of the home, sequestering the Bedroom wing and providing access to the Kitchen and Breakfast Room
■ This home is designed with a slab foundation

MAIN FLOOR — 2,551 SQ. FT.
GARAGE — 642 SQ. FT.

TOTAL LIVING AREA:
2,551 SQ. FT.

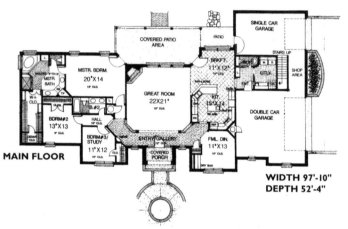

MAIN FLOOR

**WIDTH 97'-10"
DEPTH 52'-4"**

Accented by Vaulted Ceilings and Columns

Price Code: D

■ This plan features
—Three bedrooms
—Two full and one half baths
■ Corner quoins, arched windows, and keystones accent the exterior
■ Columns define the entrances to the Dining Room, Family Room and Breakfast Room
■ Vaulted ceilings adding volume to the Foyer, Dining Room, Living Room, Family Room, Breakfast Room and the Master Bath
■ An efficient and well-appointed Kitchen highlighted by serving bar to the Family Room
■ A large focal point fireplace enhances the Family Room
■ Private Master Suite is topped by a tray ceiling and enhanced by a lavish Bath
■ Two additional Bedrooms share the full Bath in the hall
■ This home is designed with basement, slab, and crawlspace foundation options

MAIN FLOOR — 2,094 SQ. FT.
BASEMENT — 2,108 SQ. FT.
GARAGE — 453 SQ. FT.

TOTAL LIVING AREA:
2,094 SQ. FT.

MAIN FLOOR

© Frank Betz Associates, Inc.

To order your Blueprints, call 1-800-235-5700

Private Master Suite

Price Code: D

■ This plan features:

— Three bedrooms

— Two full and one half bath

■ Secluded Master Suite tucked into the rear left corner of the home with a luxurious Bath

■ Two additional Bedrooms at the opposite side of the home sharing the full hall Bath

■ Expansive Living Room highlighted by a corner fireplace and access to the rear Porch

■ Kitchen is sandwiched between the bright, bayed Nook and the formal Dining Room

■ This home is designed with slab and crawlspace foundation options

MAIN FLOOR — 2,069 SQ. FT.
GARAGE — 481 SQ. FT.

TOTAL LIVING AREA:
2,069 SQ. FT.

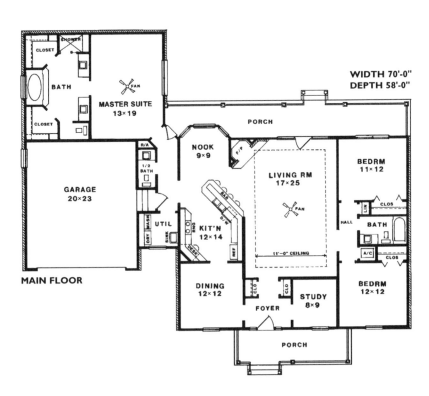

WIDTH 70'-0"
DEPTH 58'-0"

CLOSET
SHOWER
BATH
MASTER SUITE
13×19
CLOSET
PORCH
R/A
NOOK
9×9
1/2 BATH
GARAGE
20×23
LIVING RM
17×25
FAN
BEDRM
11×12
LIN CLOS
HALL
BATH
A/C CLOS
UTIL
DRY WASH
SINK
KIT'N
12×14
11'-0" CEILING
REF
MAIN FLOOR
DINING
12×12
CLO
CLO
STUDY
8×9
BEDRM
12×12
FOYER
PORCH

Sunny and Bright

Price Code: C

■ This plan features:

— Three bedrooms

— Two full baths

■ The front Porch offers a great place to sit and watch the world pass by

■ The Kitchen will get plenty of light, thanks to the adjoining turret-style Breakfast Area

■ The Great Room features a sloped ceiling, a focal point fireplace, and access to the Deck

■ A split-Bedroom design is popular for those craving a private retreat

■ The Master Bedroom Suite includes a large walk-in closet and a Bathroom with all the amenities

■ This home is designed with a basement foundation

MAIN FLOOR — 1,990 SQ. FT.
BASEMENT — 1,338 SQ. FT.
GARAGE — 660 SQ. FT.

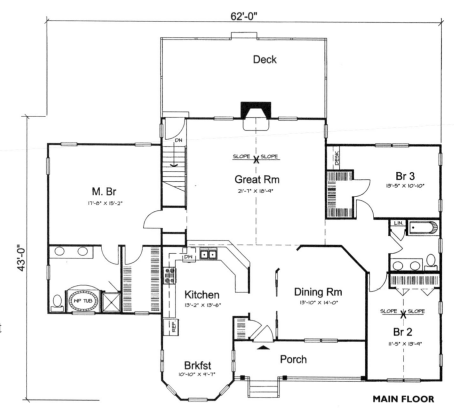

62'-0"

43'-0"

Deck

Great Rm
21'-7" X 18'-4"

M. Br
17'-8" X 15'-2"

Br 3
13'-5" X 10'-10"

Kitchen
13'-2" X 13'-6"

Dining Rm
13'-10" X 14'-0"

Br 2
11'-5" X 13'-4"

Brkfst
10'-10" X 9'-7"

Porch

MAIN FLOOR

TOTAL LIVING AREA:
1,990 SQ. FT.

76

To order your Blueprints, call 1-800-235-5700

Stylistic Symmetry

Price Code: H

■ This plan features:
— Three bedrooms
— Two full and one half baths

■ The symmetrical front Porch is set off by ionic columns, stylistic balustrades and fancy fretwork

■ Fish-scale accents, twin louvered dormers and a brick chimney add to the design's Victorian-heritage style

■ The Breakfast Nook brings natural light from from the rear Porch into this casual eating area

■ Interior columns separate the Dining Room from the Great Room, which boasts a coffered ceiling, a fireplace, and lush built-in cabinetry

■ This home is designed with a crawlspace foundation

■ Alternate foundation options available at an additional charge. Please call 1-800-235-5700 for more information.

MAIN FLOOR — 2,329 SQ. FT.
GARAGE — 528 SQ. FT.

TOTAL LIVING AREA:
2,329 SQ. FT.

MAIN FLOOR

WIDTH 72'-0"
DEPTH 73'-4"

Classic Ranch has Contemporary Flavor

Price Code: A

■ This plan features:
— Three bedrooms
— One full and one three-quarter baths

■ A galley-styled Kitchen easily serving the Dining Room

■ A Living Room with bump out window and fireplace

■ A Master Bedroom with a private Bath and an individual shower

■ This home is designed with basement, slab, and crawlspace foundation options

MAIN FLOOR — 1,268 SQ. FT.
BASEMENT — 1,248 SQ. FT.

TOTAL LIVING AREA:
1,268 SQ. FT.

MAIN FLOOR

OPTIONAL CRAWLSPACE/SLAB

To order your Blueprints, call 1-800-235-5700

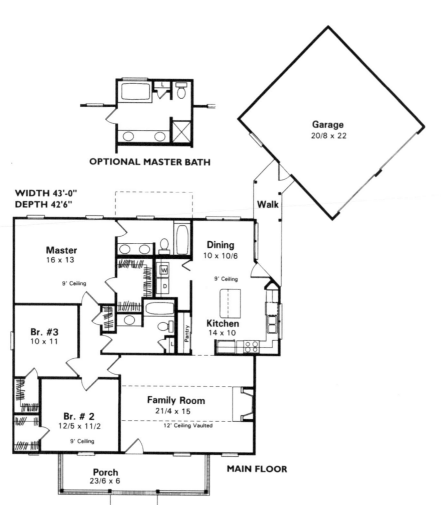

OPTIONAL MASTER BATH

Garage
20/8 x 22

Walk

WIDTH 43'-0"
DEPTH 42'6"

Master
16 x 13

9' Ceiling

Dining
10 x 10/6

9' Ceiling

Br. #3
10 x 11

Kitchen
14 x 10

Pantry

Br. # 2
12/5 x 11/2

9' Ceiling

Family Room
21/4 x 15

12' Ceiling Vaulted

Porch
23/6 x 6

MAIN FLOOR

Easy Living

Price Code: A

- ■ This plan features:
- — Three bedrooms
- — Two full baths
- ■ A covered front Porch shelters the entry to this home
- ■ Family Room is enlarged by vaulted ceiling above a cozy fireplace
- ■ The L-shaped Kitchen includes a work island and Dining Area
- ■ The Master Bedroom has two building options for its Bath
- ■ Both of the secondary Bedrooms have walk-in closets
- ■ This home is designed with slab and crawlspace foundation options

MAIN FLOOR — 1,474 SQ. FT.
GARAGE — 454 SQ. FT.

TOTAL LIVING AREA:
1,474 SQ. FT.

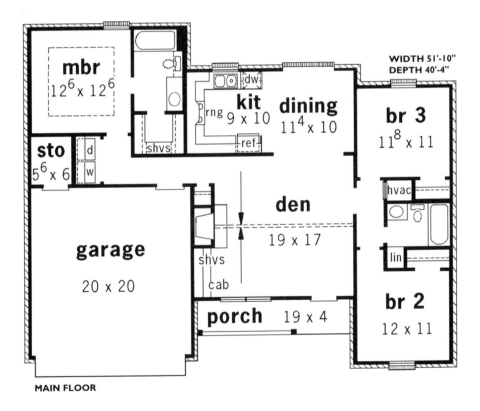

WIDTH 51'-10"
DEPTH 40'-4"

mbr
12⁶ x 12⁶

sto
5⁶ x 6

garage
20 x 20

kit
9 x 10

dining
11⁴ x 10

den
19 x 17

shvs

cab

porch   19 x 4

br 3
11⁸ x 11

hvac

lin

br 2
12 x 11

shvs

rng

ref

dw

d
w

MAIN FLOOR

Private Master Suite

Price Code: A

■ This plan features:

— Three bedrooms

— Two full baths

■ A spacious Den enhanced by a vaulted ceiling and fireplace

■ A well-equipped Kitchen with windowed-double sink

■ A secluded Master Suite with decorative ceiling, private Bath, and walk-in closet with shelves

■ Two additional Bedrooms sharing hall Bath

■ This home is designed with a slab foundation

MAIN FLOOR — 1,293 SQ. FT.
GARAGE — 433 SQ. FT.

TOTAL LIVING AREA:
1,293 SQ. FT.

Turret Study
Creates Impact

Price Code: I

■ This plan features:

—Three bedrooms

—Two full, one half, and
one three-quarter baths

■ Entry doors opening into the
formal Living Room leading to
the Lanai through sliding glass
doors and a mitered glass corner

■ Spacious Master Suite including
a fireplace, Morning Kitchen Bar,
and Lanai access

■ This home is designed with a
slab foundation

■ Alternate foundation options
available at an additional charge.
Please call 1-800-235-5700 for
more information.

MAIN FLOOR — 3,477 SQ. FT.
GARAGE — 771 SQ. FT.

TOTAL LIVING AREA:
3,477 SQ. FT.

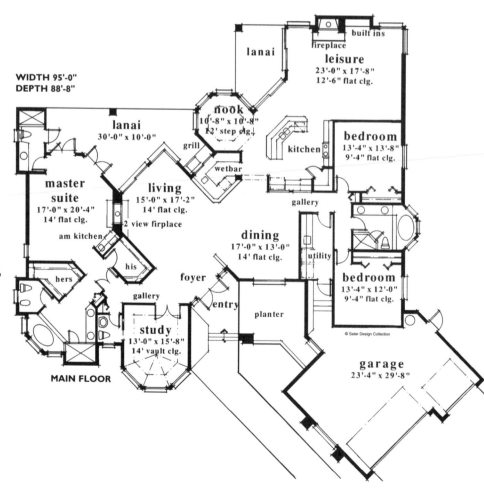

WIDTH 95'-0"
DEPTH 88'-8"

built ins
fireplace
lanai
leisure
23'-0" x 17'-8"
12'-6" flat clg.

nook
10'-8" x 10'-8"
12' step clg.
grill
kitchen
bedroom
13'-4" x 13'-8"
9'-4" flat clg.

lanai
30'-0" x 10'-0"
wetbar

master
suite
17'-0" x 20'-4"
14' flat clg.
living
15'-0" x 17'-2"
14' flat clg.
gallery

am kitchen
2 view fireplace
dining
17'-0" x 13'-0"
14' flat clg.
utility

hers
his
foyer
bedroom
13'-4" x 12'-0"
9'-4" flat clg.

gallery
entry
planter

study
13'-0" x 15'-8"
14' vault clg.
© Sater Design Collection

MAIN FLOOR
garage
23'-4" x 29'-8"

80

To order your Blueprints, call 1-800-235-5700

WIDTH 50'-0"
DEPTH 55'-4"

MAIN FLOOR

© Frank Betz Associates, Inc.

GARAGE LOCATION W/ BASEMENT

BASEMENT STAIRS LOCATION
OPTION

With All the Amenities

Price Code: C

■ This plan features:

— Three bedrooms

— Two full and one half baths

■ 16-foot ceiling over the Foyer

■ Great Room showcasing decorative columns at its arched entrance and French door to the rear yard

■ Vaulted ceiling in Dining Room

■ Expansive Kitchen features a center work island and a built-in Pantry and Breakfast Area

■ This home is designed with basement, slab, and crawlspace foundation options

MAIN FLOOR — 1,884 SQ. FT.
BASEMENT — 1,908 SQ. FT.
GARAGE — 495 SQ. FT.

TOTAL LIVING AREA:
1,884 SQ. FT.

Awesome Artistry

Price Code: C

■ This plan features:

— Three bedrooms

— Two full and one half baths

■ Stone and wood, combined with decorative arched windows and multiple gables

■ The Great Room features decorative windows letting in plenty of natural light, a focal point fireplace, and columns gracing each of its entrances

■ Columns also adorn the entrance to the formal Dining Room, which has a wall of windows and a view of the rear Deck

■ This home is designed with basement, crawlspace and slab foundation options

MAIN FLOOR — 2,161 SQ. FT.
BASEMENT — 2,161 SQ. FT.
GARAGE — 590 SQ. FT.

TOTAL LIVING AREA:
2,161 SQ. FT.

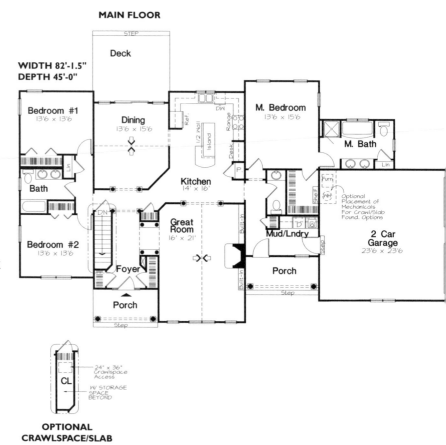

MAIN FLOOR

WIDTH 82'-1.5"
DEPTH 45'-0"

**OPTIONAL
CRAWLSPACE/SLAB**

To order your Blueprints, call 1-800-235-5700

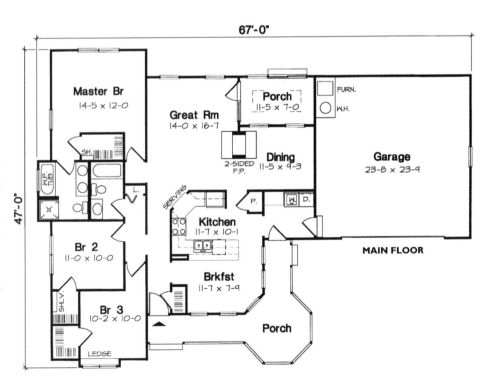

67'-0"

47'-0"

Master Br
14-5 x 12-0

Great Rm
14-0 x 16-7

Porch
11-5 x 7-0

FURN.

W.H.

SH.

W.P.
TUB

L.

2-SIDED
F.P.

Dining
11-5 x 9-3

Garage
23-8 x 23-9

SERVING

Br 2
11-0 x 10-0

P.

W D.

Kitchen
11-7 x 10-1

MAIN FLOOR

SHLV.

Br 3
10-2 x 10-0

Brkfst
11-7 x 7-9

LEDGE

Porch

Gazebo Porch Creates Vintage Feel

Price Code: A

■ This plan features:

— Three bedrooms

— Two full baths

■ An old-fashioned welcome is created by the covered Porch

■ The Breakfast Area overlooks the Porch and is separated from the Kitchen by an extended counter

■ The Dining Room and the Great Room are highlighted by a two-sided fireplace

■ The roomy Master Suite is enhanced by a whirlpool tub and a walk-in closet

■ This home is designed with slab and crawlspace foundation options

MAIN FLOOR — 1,452 SQ. FT.
GARAGE — 584 SQ. FT.

TOTAL LIVING AREA:
1,452 SQ. FT.

Spectacular Front Window

Price Code: C

■ This plan features:

— Three bedrooms

— Two full baths

■ The Family Room has a vaulted ceiling and is accented by a fireplace

■ The Master Suite features a tray ceiling over the Bedroom and a vaulted ceiling over the Bath

■ This home is designed with basement, slab, and crawlspace foundation options

MAIN FLOOR — 1,875 SQ. FT.
BASEMENT — 1,891 SQ. FT.
GARAGE — 475 SQ. FT.

TOTAL LIVING AREA:
1,875 SQ. FT.

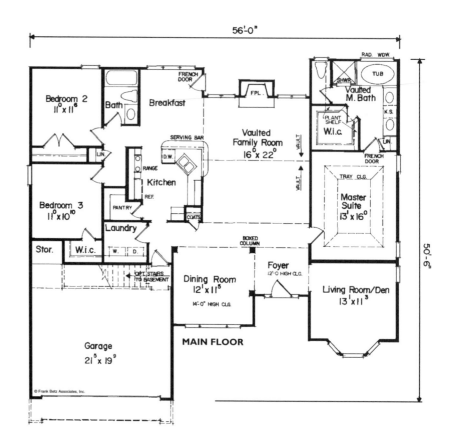

56'-0"

50'-6"

Bedroom 2
11⁰ x 11⁶

Bath

Breakfast

FRENCH DOOR

FPL.

RAD. WDW.

SHWR

TUB

Vaulted M. Bath

K.S.

PLANT SHELF

W.i.c.

LIN

FRENCH DOOR

SERVING BAR

D.W.

Vaulted Family Room
16⁰ x 22⁰

VAULT

VAULT

RANGE

Kitchen

REF.

TRAY CLG.

Bedroom 3
11⁰ x 10¹⁰

PANTRY

COATS

Master Suite
13' x 16⁰

Laundry

Stor.

W.i.c.

W.

D.

OPT. STAIRS TO BASEMENT

BOXED COLUMN

Foyer
12'-0 HIGH CLG.

Dining Room
12' x 11⁵

14'-0" HIGH CLG.

Living Room/Den
13' x 11³

Garage
21⁵ x 19⁹

MAIN FLOOR

© Frank Betz Associates, Inc.

Wrapping Porch
Highlights Ranch

Price Code: B

- This plan features:
 — Three bedrooms
 — Two full baths
- The front elevation is adorned with a wrapping Porch
- The expansive Family Room flows into the Dining Area, which in turn opens to the Kitchen
- The Master Suite includes a recessed ceiling and a private five-piece Bath
- Two additional Bedrooms share a full hall Bath
- This home is designed with slab and crawlspace foundation options

MAIN FLOOR — 1,550 SQ. FT.
GARAGE — 548 SQ. FT.

TOTAL LIVING AREA:
1,550 SQ. FT.

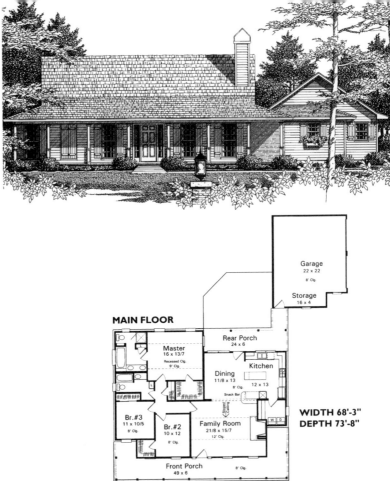

WIDTH 68'-3"
DEPTH 73'-8"

Decorative Ceilings
add Accents

Price Code: C

- This plan features:
 — Three bedrooms
 — Two full baths
- The cozy front Porch leads into the formal Foyer
- A secluded Study is to the right of the Foyer
- Colonial columns and a half wall grace the entrance of the Dining Area
- The Great Room is accented by a fireplace and a tray ceiling
- The Kitchen is laid out in an efficient U-shape and features an extended counter/eating bar
- The Master Suite is tucked into the left rear corner of the home
- A tray ceiling highlights the Master Bedroom
- Two additional Bedrooms, located on the opposite side of the home, share a full hall Bath
- This home is designed with slab and crawlspace foundation options

MAIN FLOOR — 1,771 SQ. FT.
GARAGE — 480 SQ. FT.

TOTAL LIVING AREA:
1,771 SQ. FT.

PLAN NO. 99284

Lots of Views and Breezes

Price Code: D

■ This plan features:
— Three bedrooms
— Two full baths
■ Kitchen directly off Foyer with cooktop/work island and serving counter/snack bar
■ Sloped ceiling tops fireplace and sliding glass doors to Terrace in Living/Dining Rooms
■ Master Bedroom enhanced by outdoor access and a pampering Bath with a whirlpool tub
■ Two additional Bedrooms share a double-vanity Bath
■ This home is designed with a slab foundation

MAIN FLOOR — 2,189 SQ. FT.

TOTAL LIVING AREA:
2,189 SQ. FT.

56'-0"

72'-0"

MAIN FLOOR

PLAN NO. 98554

Covered Patio

Price Code: D

■ This plan features:
— Four bedrooms
— Three full baths
■ The Great Room and Breakfast Nook share a free-flowing space that offers access to the Covered Patio
■ The Master Suite features a sloped ceiling, walk-in closet, and Bath with a double vanity and whirlpool tub
■ This home is designed with a slab foundation

MAIN FLOOR — 2,169 SQ. FT.
GARAGE — 542 SQ. FT.

TOTAL LIVING AREA:
2,169 SQ. FT.

WIDTH 76'-6"
DEPTH 44'-4"

MAIN FLOOR

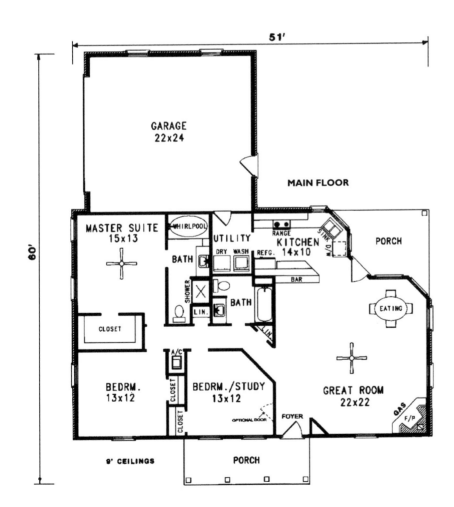

GARAGE
22x24

MAIN FLOOR

51'

60'

MASTER SUITE
15x13

WHIRLPOOL

UTILITY

BATH

DRY WASH

RANGE

KITCHEN
14x10

REFG.

SINK D.W.

PORCH

SHOWER

BATH

LIN.

BAR

EATING

CLOSET

A/C

BEDRM.
13x12

CLOSET

CLOSET

BEDRM./STUDY
13x12

LIN.

OPTIONAL DOOR

FOYER

GREAT ROOM
22x22

GAS
F/P

9' CEILINGS

PORCH

Cozy Three Bedroom

Price Code: B

■ This plan features:

— Three bedrooms

— Two full baths

■ The triple-arched front Porch adds to the curb appeal of the home

■ The expansive Great Room is accented by a cozy gas fireplace

■ The Master Suite is highlighted by a walk-in closet and a whirlpool Bath

■ Two secondary Bedrooms share use of the full hall Bath

■ The rear Porch extends dining to the outdoors

■ This home is designed with slab and crawlspace foundation options

MAIN FLOOR — 1,515 SQ. FT.
GARAGE — 528 SQ. FT.

TOTAL LIVING AREA:
1,515 SQ. FT.

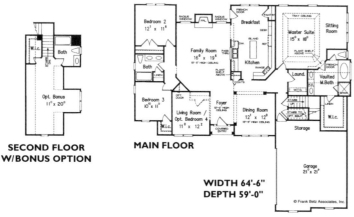

PLAN NO. 98466

Master Suite Sitting Room

Price Code: D

- This plan features:
— Four bedrooms
— Three full baths
- The Living Room can be open to the Foyer or can be altered for use as a Bedroom by placing a door off the hall
- The Master Suite includes a Sitting Area, a full Bath, and a walk-in closet
- This home is designed with basement, slab, and crawlspace foundation options

MAIN FLOOR — 2,193 SQ. FT.
GARAGE — 522 SQ. FT.
BONUS — 400 SQ. FT.
BASEMENT — 2,193 SQ. FT.

TOTAL LIVING AREA:
2,193 SQ. FT.

SECOND FLOOR W/BONUS OPTION

MAIN FLOOR

WIDTH 64'-6"
DEPTH 59'-0"

© Frank Betz Associates, Inc.

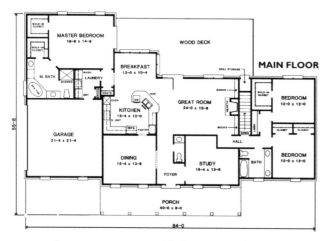

PLAN NO. 90461

Columned Elegance

Price Code: E

- This plan features:
— Three bedrooms
— Two full baths
- This traditional home is enhanced by elegant columns on the large front Porch
- The Study and the Dining Room both overlook the front Porch
- The Great Room has a fireplace, built-in bookshelves and access to the rear Deck
- The modern Kitchen has an angled serving bar with a double sink
- The Breakfast Nook has a bright wall of windows that overlooks the rear yard
- The secluded Master Suite has dual walk-in closets, and a Bath with a spa tub
- Two additional Bedrooms are located on the opposite side of the home, and share a full Bath
- This home is designed with basement and crawlspace foundation options

MAIN FLOOR — 2,485 SQ. FT.
BASEMENT — 2,485 SQ. FT.
GARAGE — 484 SQ. FT.

TOTAL LIVING AREA:
2,485 SQ. FT.

MAIN FLOOR

To order your Blueprints, call 1-800-235-5700

Traditionally-Styled Country Home

Price Code: H

■ This plan features:
— Three bedrooms
— Two full and one half baths
■ Split-shake accents top gables of clapboard siding on this traditionally-styled Country home
■ Double-column symmetry of the front Porch makes a perfect landing for rocking chairs
■ Specialty ceilings, interior columns, archways, and numerous built-ins really complement the multi-pane windows
■ His and her walk-in closets, whirlpool tub, and walk-in shower with shampoo niche enhance the Master Suite
■ This home is designed with a crawlspace foundation
■ Alternate foundations available at an additional cost. Please call 1-800-235-5700 for more information.

MAIN FLOOR — 2,555 SQ. FT.

TOTAL LIVING AREA:
2,555 SQ. FT.

WIDTH 70'-0"
DEPTH 76'-6"

MAIN FLOOR

Fireplace Adds a Cozy Touch

Price Code: B

■ This plan features:
— Three bedrooms
— Two full baths
■ A Garage level that includes a basement recreation and workshop area, perfect for the household hobbyist
■ A large bow window and a wide opening to the formal Dining Room, adding to the feeling of spaciousness in the Living Room
■ Access to a raised Deck from the spacious Kitchen
■ This home is designed with a basement foundation

MAIN FLOOR — 1,676 SQ. FT.
BASEMENT — 592 SQ. FT.
WORKSHOP — 144 SQ. FT.
GARAGE — 697 SQ. FT.

TOTAL LIVING AREA:
1,676 SQ. FT.

REAR ELEVATION

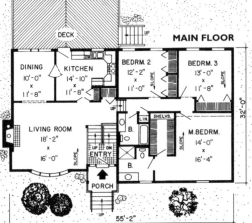

MAIN FLOOR

Split-Bedroom Ranch

Price Code: C

■ This plan features:

— Three bedrooms

— Two full baths

■ The Foyer opens into the Great Room with a vaulted ceiling and a hearth fireplace

■ The U-shaped Kitchen is located between the Dining Room and the Breakfast Nook

■ The secluded Master Bedroom is spacious and includes a full Bath

■ The covered front Porch and rear Deck provide additional space for entertaining

■ This home is designed with basement, slab, and crawlspace foundation options

MAIN FLOOR — 1,804 SQ. FT.
BASEMENT — 1,804 SQ. FT.
GARAGE — 506 SQ. FT.

TOTAL LIVING AREA:
1,804 SQ. FT.

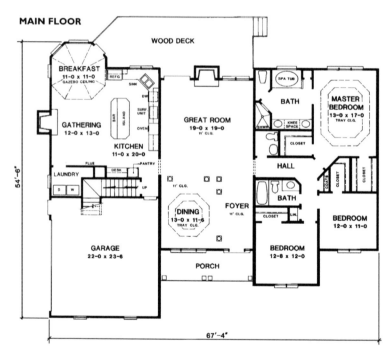

MAIN FLOOR

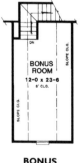

BONUS

To order your Blueprints, call 1-800-235-5700

Easy Everyday Living

Price Code: B

■ This plan features:

— Three bedrooms

— Two full baths

■ Front entrance accented by segmented arches, sidelight, and transom windows

■ Open Living Room with fireplace and wetbar

■ Dining Area open to both the Living Room and Kitchen

■ Efficient Kitchen with a cooktop island and a walk-in Pantry

■ Master Suite features a large walk-in closet, double-vanity Bath, and access to Patio

■ This home is designed with basement, slab, and crawlspace foundation options

MAIN FLOOR — 1,664 SQ. FT.
BASEMENT — 1,600 SQ. FT.
GARAGE — 440 SQ. FT

TOTAL LIVING AREA:
1,664 SQ. FT.

Floor plan labels:

48'-0"

63'-0"

MstrBed 13x17

Master

Patio

LivRm 18x20 10'Ceiling

Bar

Bed#3 11x13

Kit 8x10

Pant

B#2

Ent

Din 10'Ceiling

Util

Por

Bed#2 11x13

Gar 20x22

MAIN FLOOR

Vaulted Ceilings
Define Public Spaces

Price Code: A

- This plan features:
  - Three bedrooms
  - Two full baths
- A Pantry adds storage to the U-shaped Kitchen
- The drive-under Garage leads up to the Great Room
- Display shelves are widely visible throughout the house
- A tray ceiling adds scale to the Master Bedroom
- Visitors are protected from the weather by a small covered Porch
- The Master Bath offers a large tub and a separate shower
- This home is designed with a basement foundation

MAIN FLOOR — 1,166 SQ. FT.
BASEMENT — 1,166 SQ. FT.

TOTAL LIVING AREA:
1,166 SQ. FT

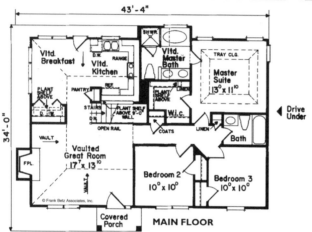

Sprawling Ranch

Price Code: D

- This plan features:
  - Three bedrooms
  - Two full and one half baths
- Foyer with a 12-foot ceiling that flows into the Dining and Living Rooms
- Family Room in rear of home with a fireplace flanked by radius windows
- The Kitchen is L-shaped and has a center island with cooktop
- The Breakfast Bay area includes a walk-in Pantry
- The Master Suite is beyond belief with a tray ceiling, a Sitting Area, a walk-in closet, and a luxurious Bath
- Two other large Bedrooms share access to a full Bath
- This home is designed with basement and crawlspace foundation options

MAIN FLOOR — 2,236 SQ. FT.
BASEMENT — 2,236 SQ. FT.
GARAGE — 517 SQ. FT.

TOTAL LIVING AREA:
2,236 SQ. FT.

To order your Blueprints, call 1-800-235-5700

One-Level Living at its Finest

Price Code: L

- This plan features:
— Four bedrooms
— Three full, one half, and one three-quarter baths
- Luxurious Master Suite includes huge closet, Bath, and Exercise Area
- All secondary Bedrooms feature private Baths and walk-in closets
- Off the rounded Breakfast Room is a covered Patio for outdoor meals
- The three-car Garage features plenty of extra storage
- A formal Dining Room features a tall pullman ceiling
- This home is designed with a slab foundation

MAIN FLOOR — 4,615 SQ. FT.
GARAGE — 748 SQ. FT.

**TOTAL LIVING AREA:
4,615 SQ. FT.**

MAIN FLOOR

**WIDTH 113'-4"
DEPTH 69'-4"**

Traditional Ranch

Price Code: B

- This plan features:
— Three bedrooms
— Two full baths
- A large front palladium window gives this home great curb appeal, and allows a view of the front yard from the Living Room
- A vaulted ceiling in the Living Room, adds to the architectural interest and the spacious feel of the room
- Sliding glass doors in the Dining Room that lead to a wood Deck
- A built-in Pantry, double sink and Breakfast Bar in the efficient Kitchen
- A Master Suite that includes a walk-in closet and a private Bath with a double vanity
- Two additional Bedrooms that share a full hall Bath
- This home is designed with basement, slab, and crawlspace foundation options

MAIN FLOOR —1,568 SQ. FT.
BASEMENT — 1,568 SQ. FT.
GARAGE — 509 SQ. FT.

**TOTAL LIVING AREA:
1,568 SQ. FT.**

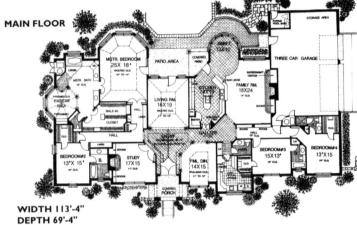

MAIN FLOOR

**OPTIONAL
CRAWLSPACE/SLAB**

Split-Bedroom Plan

Price Code: D

■ This plan features:

— Three bedrooms

— Two full baths

■ Dining Room is crowned by a tray ceiling

■ Living Room/Den is privatized by double doors at its entrance

■ The Kitchen includes a walk-in Pantry and a corner double sink

■ The Master Suite is topped by volume ceilings and contains a compartmental Bath

■ This home is designed with basement, slab, and crawlspace foundation options

MAIN FLOOR — 2,051 SQ. FT.
BASEMENT — 2,051 SQ. FT.
GARAGE — 441 SQ. FT.

TOTAL LIVING AREA:
2,051 SQ. FT.

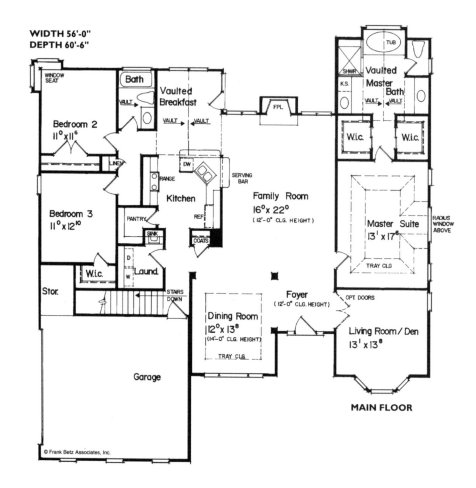

WIDTH 56'-0"
DEPTH 60'-6"

© Frank Betz Associates, Inc.

MAIN FLOOR

94

PLAN NO. 90423

Expansive,
Not Expensive

Price Code: C

■ This plan features:

— Three bedrooms

— Two full baths

■ A Master Suite with his and her closets and a private Master Bath

■ Two additional Bedrooms that share a full Bath with Dressing Area

■ A pleasant Dining Room that overlooks a rear garden

■ A well-equipped Kitchen with a large Pantry and serving counter

■ This home is designed with basement, slab, and crawlspace foundation options

MAIN FLOOR — 1,773 SQ. FT.

TOTAL LIVING AREA:
1,773 SQ. FT.

Luxury in One-story Plan

Price Code: B

■ This plan features:

— Three bedrooms

— Two full baths

■ Covered Stoop leads into dynamic Activity Room with fireplace, recessed ceiling, and adjacent Dining Room and Sun Deck

■ Open Kitchen/Breakfast Room offers loads of counter space and light with nearby Pantry, Laundry, and Garage

■ This home is designed with basement, slab, and crawlspace foundation options

MAIN FLOOR — 1,595 SQ. FT.
BASEMENT — 1,595 SQ. FT.
GARAGE — 491 SQ. FT.

TOTAL LIVING AREA:
1,595 SQ. FT.

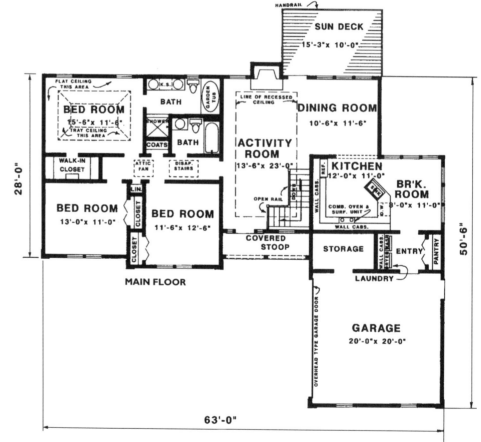

To order your Blueprints, call 1-800-235-5700

Keystone and Arched Windows

Price Code: B

- This plan features:
  — Three bedrooms
  — Two full baths
- An arched window in the Dining Room offers eye-catching appeal
- A fireplace and French door to the rear yard grace the Great Room
- An efficient Kitchen includes a serving bar, Pantry, and pass-through to the Great Room
- A plush Master Suite includes a private Bath and walk-in closet
- This home is designed with basement, slab, and crawlspace foundation options

MAIN FLOOR — 1,670 SQ. FT.
GARAGE — 240 SQ. FT.

TOTAL LIVING AREA:
1,670 SQ. FT.

Open and Airy

Price Code: C

- This plan features:
  — Three bedrooms
  — Two full baths
- Less formal and more spacious, the Family Room is a contemporary masterpiece
- A corner window, walk-in closet, and soaking tub make the Master Suite complete
- While the family's young, the Study can double as a Nursery
- A gourmet Kitchen looks straight through the Breakfast Area's bay window to views beyond
- This home is designed with a slab foundation

MAIN FLOOR — 1,869 SQ. FT.
GARAGE — 470 SQ. FT.

TOTAL LIVING AREA:
1,869 SQ. FT.

WIDTH 61'-8"
DEPTH 53'-0"
MAIN FLOOR

Gracefully Adorned

Price Code: H

- This plan features:
  — Three Bedrooms
  — Two and one half Baths

- Artistic balustrades, patterned trim work, fashionable gables and multi-faceted exteriors gracefully adorn this home

- Glass panel double doors lead to a spacious Foyer that adjoins a stepped ceiling Dining Room to the right and a beamed ceiling Study to the left

- The Great Room which is highlighted by a fireplace, flanked with built-in shelving, and three sets of French doors to the rear Porch

- This home is designed with a crawlspace foundation

- Alternate foundations available at an additional charge. Please call 1-800-235-5700 for more information.

MAIN FLOOR — 2,555 SQ. FT.
GARAGE — 640 SQ. FT.

TOTAL LIVING AREA:
2,555 SQ. FT.

MAIN FLOOR

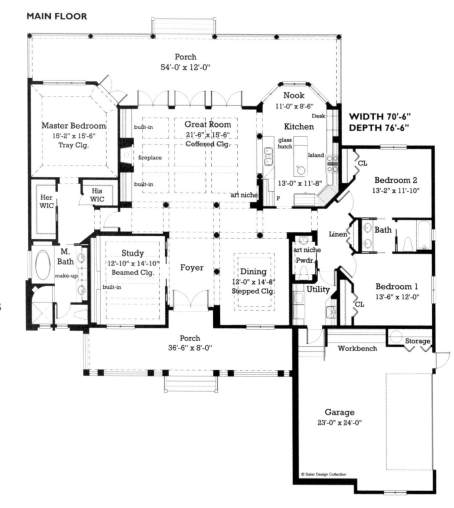

WIDTH 70'-6"
DEPTH 76'-6"

To order your Blueprints, call 1-800-235-5700

Elegant Brick Exterior

Price Code: A

■ This plan features:

—Three bedrooms

—Two full baths

■ Detailing and accenting columns highlighting the covered front Porch

■ Den enhanced by a corner fireplace and adjoining Dining Room

■ Efficient, well-appointed Kitchen with easy access to the Utility/Laundry Room

■ Master Bedroom topped by a vaulted ceiling featuring a private Bath and walk-in closet

■ This home is designed with slab and crawlspace foundation options

MAIN FLOOR — 1,390 SQ. FT.
GARAGE — 590 SQ. FT.

TOTAL LIVING AREA:
1,390 SQ. FT.

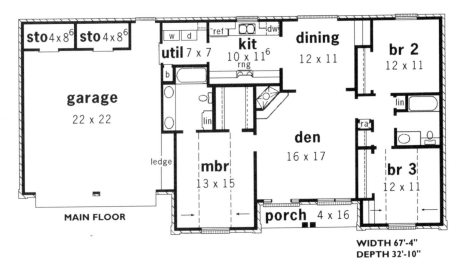

MAIN FLOOR

WIDTH 67'-4"
DEPTH 32'-10"

Home for the Discriminating Buyer

Price Code: B

■ This plan features:

— Three bedrooms

— Two full baths

■ A sloped ceiling and a corner fireplace enhancing the Great Room

■ A Kitchen with a garden window above the double sink

■ A peninsula counter joining the Kitchen and the Breakfast Room

■ A Master Suite with a large walk-in closet, a private Bath with an oval corner tub, separate shower and double vanity

■ This home is designed with a basement foundation

MAIN FLOOR — 1,746 SQ. FT.
BASEMENT — 1,560 SQ. FT.
GARAGE — 455 SQ. FT.

TOTAL LIVING AREA:
1,746 SQ. FT.

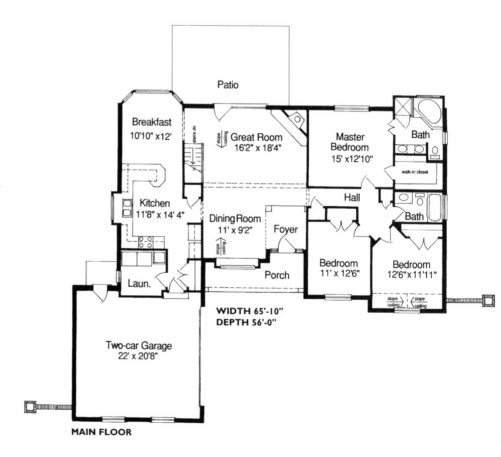

MAIN FLOOR

WIDTH 65'-10"
DEPTH 56'-0"

To order your Blueprints, call 1-800-235-5700

Bricks and Arches
Detail this Ranch

Price Code: F

■ This plan features:

— Two bedrooms

— Two full and one half baths

■ A Master Bedroom with a luxurious Bath complimented by a skylit walk-in closet

■ A Great Room sharing a see-through fireplace with the Hearth Room

■ A Gazebo-shaped nook opening into the Kitchen with a center island, snack bar and desk

■ This home is designed with a basement foundation

■ Alternate foundation options available at an additional charge. Please call 1-800-235-5700 for more information.

MAIN FLOOR — 2,512 SQ. FT.
GARAGE — 783 SQ. FT.

TOTAL LIVING AREA:
2,512 SQ. FT.

MAIN FLOOR

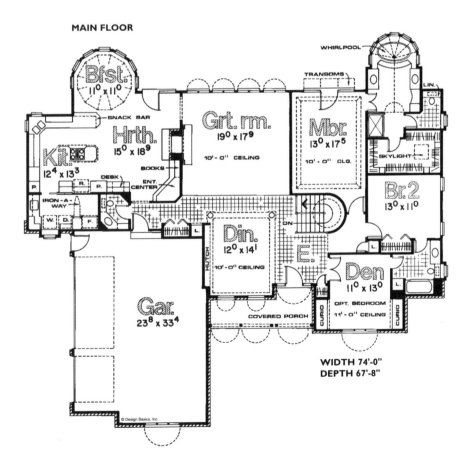

WHIRLPOOL

TRANSOMS

Bfst.
11⁰ x 11⁰

SNACK BAR

Grt. rm.
19⁰ x 17⁹
10'-0" CEILING

Mbr.
13⁰ x 17⁵
10'-0" CLG.

LIN.

Hrth.
15⁰ x 18⁹

SKYLIGHT

Kit.
12⁴ x 13³

BOOKS

Br. 2
13⁰ x 11⁰

DESK

ENT. CENTER

IRON-A-WAY

Din.
12⁰ x 14¹
10'-0" CEILING

Den
11⁰ x 13⁰

HUTCH

Gar.
23⁸ x 33⁴

OPT. BEDROOM
11'-0" CEILING

CURIO

CURIO

COVERED PORCH

© Design Basics, Inc.

WIDTH 74'-0"
DEPTH 67'-8"

Traditional Simplicity

Price Code: F

■ This plan features:

— Three bedrooms

— Two full baths

■ Twin dormers add a touch of class to this single story farmhouse

■ Gallery Porches open the indoors to nature

■ Stepped ceilings and an open floor plan give the illusion of greater overall living area in the Great Room and the Dining Room

■ A split-Bedroom plan gives the Master Suite more privacy

■ This home is designed with a crawl space foundation

■ Alternate foundation options available at an additional charge. Please call 1-800-235-5700 for more information.

MAIN FLOOR — 1,487 SQ. FT.
GARAGE — 567 SQ. FT.

TOTAL LIVING AREA:
1,487 SQ. FT.

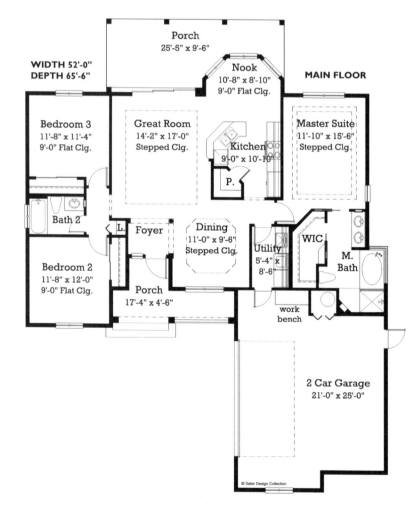

WIDTH 52'-0"
DEPTH 65'-6"

MAIN FLOOR

Porch
25'-5" x 9'-6"

Nook
10'-8" x 8'-10"
9'-0" Flat Clg.

Bedroom 3
11'-8" x 11'-4"
9'-0" Flat Clg.

Great Room
14'-2" x 17'-0"
Stepped Clg.

Kitchen
9'-0" x 10'-10"

Master Suite
11'-10" x 15'-6"
Stepped Clg.

P.

Bath 2

L.

Foyer

Dining
11'-0" x 9'-6"
Stepped Clg.

Utility
5'-4" x
8'-6"

WIC

M.
Bath

Bedroom 2
11'-8" x 12'-0"
9'-0" Flat Clg.

Porch
17'-4" x 4'-6"

work
bench

2 Car Garage
21'-0" x 25'-0"

© Sater Design Collection

To order your Blueprints, call 1-800-235-5700

Offering an Inviting Welcome

Price Code: F

- This plan features:
  - Three bedrooms
  - Two full baths
- A sidelight borders the oval-glass Entry door that opens onto the Foyer with dramatic arches and stately columns
- Fish-scale siding, detailed trim work, and louvered shutters accent this Victorian-style farmhouse
- Stepped ceilings in the Great Room and Dining room help enlarge the sense of space
- Household chores are easily tended to in the ample Utility Room or at the built-in workbench in the Garage
- The private Master Suite, complemented with a stepped ceiling, features a deluxe Master Bath with a corner glass wall and whirlpool tub
- This home is designed with a crawlspace foundation
- Alternate foundation options available at an additional charge. Please call 1-800-235-5700 for more information.

MAIN FLOOR — 1,487 SQ. FT.
GARAGE — 567 SQ. FT.

TOTAL LIVING AREA:
1,487 SQ. FT.

WIDTH 52'-6"
DEPTH 66'-0"

MAIN FLOOR

Exclusive Master Suite

Price Code: C

- This plan features:
  - Three bedrooms
  - Two full and one half baths
- Front Porch opens into Foyer and open Living and Dining Room
- Huge fireplace and double window highlight Living Room
- Convenient Kitchen with cooktop island/snack bar, Pantry, and bright Breakfast Area with backyard access
- Corner Master Bedroom offers a decorative ceiling, walk-in closets, and a double-vanity Bath
- Two additional Bedrooms with ample closets and private access to a full Bath
- This home is designed with basement, slab, and crawlspace foundation options

MAIN FLOOR — 1,831 SQ. FT.
BASEMENT — 1,831 SQ.
GARAGE — 484 SQ. FT.

TOTAL LIVING AREA:
1,831 SQ. FT.

MAIN FLOOR

OPTIONAL
CRAWLSPACE/SLAB

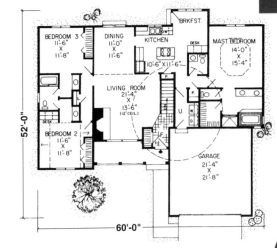

Wonderful Open Spaces

Price Code: A

■ This plan features:
— Three bedrooms
— Two full baths
■ A Family Room, Kitchen, and Breakfast Area flowing together
■ A central fireplace adds warmth and atmosphere to the Family Room, Kitchen, and the Breakfast Area
■ The Master Suite includes a walk-in closet, a double-vanity, separate shower and a tub
■ A wooden Deck that can be accessed from the Breakfast Area
■ This home is designed with slab and crawlspace foundation options

MAIN FLOOR — 1,388 SQ. FT.
GARAGE— 400 SQ. FT.

TOTAL LIVING AREA:
1,388 SQ. FT.

WIDTH 48'-0"
DEPTH 46'-0"

MAIN FLOOR

Respectively Raised

Price Code: C

■ This plan features:
— Three bedrooms
— Two full baths
■ The elevated covered Porch offers a grand-scale welcome
■ A corner fireplace casts its glow over the open design of the Grand Room, Kitchen, and Breakfast Area
■ Windows line the rear of the home, filtering light through the rooms
■ The Bedrooms, including the impressive Master Suite, and Laundry form the left wing
■ Isolated in the front of the home, the formal Dining Room provides a private eating experience
■ This home is designed with a basement foundation

MAIN FLOOR — 1,782 SQ. FT.
BONUS — 432 SQ. FT.
BASEMENT — 288 SQ. FT.
GARAGE — 828 SQ. FT.

TOTAL LIVING AREA:
1,782 SQ. FT.

MAIN FLOOR

WIDTH 50'-0"
DEPTH 42'-0"

To order your Blueprints, call 1-800-235-5700

A Grand Plan

Price Code: D

■ This plan features:

— Three bedrooms

— Two full baths

■ The Kitchen includes ample storage and work space, and offers easy access to the Breakfast Nook and the formal Dining Room

■ The Breakfast Nook has sliding doors leading to the rear yard

■ The Master Suite is in one corner of the house, offering a private retreat when needed

■ This home is designed with basement, slab, and crawlspace foundation options

MAIN FLOOR — 2,172 SQ. FT.
BASEMENT — 2,172 SQ. FT.
GARAGE — 623 SQ. FT.

TOTAL LIVING AREA:
2,172 SQ. FT.

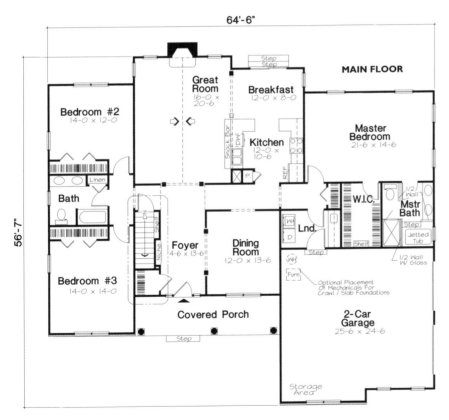

Country Ranch

Price Code: A

■ This plan features:

— Three bedrooms

— Two full baths

■ A covered, wraparound Porch, adding charm to this Country-styled home

■ A high vaulted ceiling in the Living Room

■ A smaller Kitchen with ample cupboard and counter space

■ A private Master Suite with a spa tub and a walk-in closet

■ A Shop and Storage Area in the two-car Garage

■ This home is designed with a crawlspace foundation

MAIN FLOOR — 1,485 SQ. FT.
GARAGE — 701 SQ. FT.

TOTAL LIVING AREA:
1,485 SQ. FT.

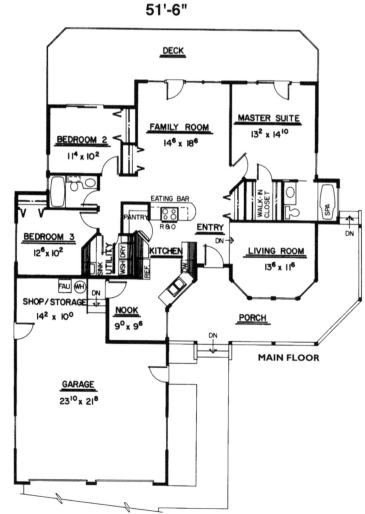

To order your Blueprints, call 1-800-235-5700

Southern Hospitality

Price Code: C

■ This plan features:

— Three bedrooms

— Two full baths

■ Welcoming Covered Veranda

■ Easy-care, tiled Entry leads into Great Room with a fieldstone fireplace and an Atrium door to another covered Veranda

■ A bright Kitchen/Dining Room includes a cooktop island/ snack bar, built-in Pantry and desk, and access to covered Veranda

■ Vaulted ceiling crowns Master Bedroom that offers a plush Bath and a huge walk-in closet

■ This home is designed with basement, slab, and crawlspace foundation options

MAIN FLOOR — 1,830 SQ. FT.
GARAGE — 759 SQ. FT.

TOTAL LIVING AREA:
1,830 SQ. FT.

WIDTH 75'-0"
DEPTH 52'-3"

COVERED VERANDA

KITCHEN/
DINING
21 X 15
9" CLGS.

MSTR.
BDRM.
14 X 16
VAULTED CLG.
9" TO 11"

SLOPED CLGS.
9" TO 11"

WALK-IN-CLOS.
9" CLGS.

H.W.
C/H
W. D.

PANTRY

HALL
9" CLGS.

LAUND.

3 CAR
GARAGE
23 X 33

DESK

REF.
O/MW.

ENT.
10" CLGS.

LIN.

BDRM #2
12 X 13
10" CLGS.

BDRM.
#3
11 X 12
9" CLGS.

GREAT
ROOM
22 X 16
CATHEDRAL CLGS.

SERVICE
PORCH

COVERED VERANDA

MAIN FLOOR

Country Couture

Price Code: H

- This plan features:
  — Three bedrooms
  — Two full baths

- The luxurious Master Suite features a bay window that provides a front-row seat to the outdoors

- The Study, with plenty of built-ins and a stepped ceiling, shares a double-sided fireplace with the Great Room

- The Great Room is the heart of this home with the fireplace, built-in bookshelves, and entertainment center

- This home is designed with a crawlspace foundation

- Alternate foundation options available at an additional charge. Please call 1-800-235-5700 for more information.

MAIN FLOOR — 2,454 SQ. FT.
BONUS ROOM — 256 SQ. FT.
GARAGE — 547 SQ. FT.

TOTAL LIVING AREA:
2,454 SQ. FT.

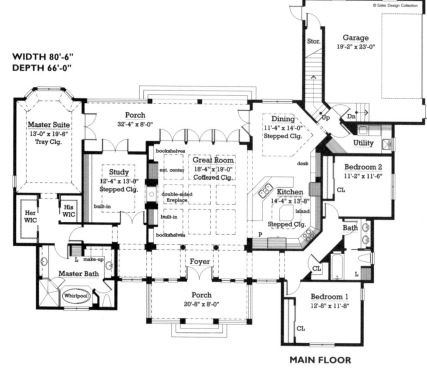

WIDTH 80'-6"
DEPTH 66'-0"

MAIN FLOOR

BONUS

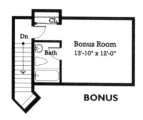

To order your Blueprints, call 1-800-235-5700

Cultured Country Living

Price Code: G

- This plan features:
  – Three bedrooms
  – Two full baths
- From the Foyer, you may detour to the Bath down one hallway or head straight into the Great Room and through the double French doors to the rear Porch
- The Great Room and adjoining Dining Room have elegant stepped ceilings
- An angled Kitchen provides all the space and amenities today's families need
- The left wing is dedicated to the Master Suite, a perfect homeowner's retreat
- Go through a double-arched front gallery to the secondary Bedrooms, located in an alcove where they share an ample Bath with dual-sink vanity
- This home is designed with a crawlspace foundation
- Alternate foundation options available at an additional charge. Please call 1-800-235-5700 for more information.

MAIN FLOOR — 1,616 SQ. FT.
BONUS — 362 SQ. FT.
GARAGE — 534 SQ. FT.

TOTAL LIVING AREA:
1,616 SQ. FT.

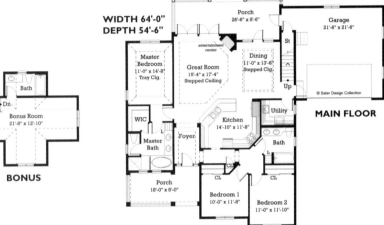

BONUS

MAIN FLOOR

WIDTH 64'-0"
DEPTH 54'-6"

Clean Country Appeal

Price Code: C

- This plan features:
  – Three bedrooms
  – Two full baths
- A vaulted-ceiling Great Room offers an impressively large family space
- Skylights flood the Great Room and Breakfast Room with natural light
- A large soaking tub in the Master Bath offers quiet comfort at the end of a long day
- The kids' wing includes a separate Bath and quick access to the covered Patio out back
- This home is designed with a slab foundation

MAIN FLOOR — 1,901 SQ. FT.
GARAGE — 484 SQ. FT.

TOTAL LIVING AREA:
1,901 SQ. FT.

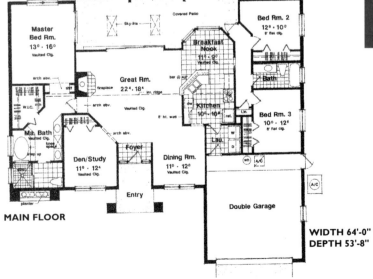

MAIN FLOOR

WIDTH 64'-0"
DEPTH 53'-8"

Gracefully Adorned

Price Code: G

■ This plan features:

— Three bedrooms

— Two full baths

■ Arched copper-topped dormers and entrances, and the classic columns and decorative fretwork provide a glowing welcome

■ The Master Bathroom includes a garden tub, walk-in shower, double vanity, linen niche and private toilet

■ The Great Room and Dining Room each are topped by a stepped ceiling

■ This home is designed with a crawlspace foundation

■ Alternate foundation options available at an additional charge. Please call 1-800-235-5700 for more information

MAIN FLOOR — 1,616 SQ. FT.

BONUS ROOM — 362 SQ. FT.

GARAGE — 534 SQ. FT.

TOTAL LIVING AREA:
1,616 SQ. FT.

WIDTH 64'-0"
DEPTH 55'-0"

MAIN FLOOR

BONUS

To order your Blueprints, call 1-800-235-5700

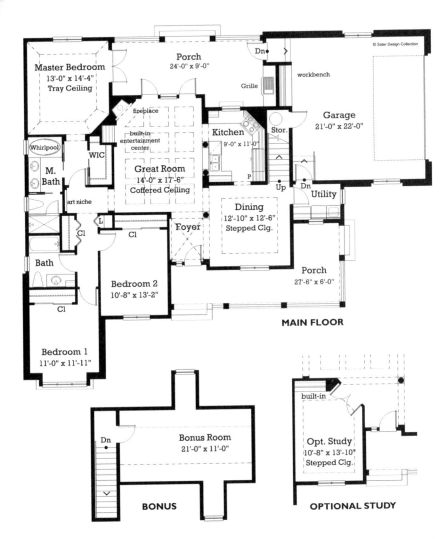

Master Bedroom
13'-0" x 14'-4"
Tray Ceiling

Porch
24'-0" x 9'-0"

Dn

workbench

Grille

Garage
21'-0" x 22'-0"

Whirlpool

fireplace

built-in
entertainment
center

Kitchen
9'-0" x 11'-0"

Stor.

WIC

M. Bath

Great Room
14'-0" x 17'-6"
Coffered Ceiling

P

Up

Dn

Utility

art niche

Dining
12'-10" x 12'-6"
Stepped Clg.

Cl

L

Cl

Cl

Foyer

Bath

Cl

Bedroom 2
10'-8" x 13'-2"

Porch
27'-6" x 6'-0"

Bedroom 1
11'-0" x 11'-11"

MAIN FLOOR

© Sater Design Collection

Dn

Bonus Room
21'-0" x 11'-0"

BONUS

built-in

Opt. Study
10'-8" x 13'-10"
Stepped Clg.

OPTIONAL STUDY

French-Country Living

Price Code: G

■ This plan features:

— Three bedrooms

— Two full baths

■ Stone, clapboard siding, detailed trimwork, and windowpanes add curb appeal

■ A corner fireplace anchors the Great Room

■ The Kitchen includes all the amenities and easy access to the Dining Room

■ The Master Suite features a large walk-in closet, whirlpool, and dual-vanity

■ This home is designed with a crawlspace foundation

■ Alternate foundation options available at an additional charge. Please call 1-800-235-5700 for more information.

MAIN FLOOR — 1,526 SQ. FT.
BONUS ROOM — 336 SQ. FT.

TOTAL LIVING AREA:
1,526 SQ. FT.

Secluded Master Suite

Price Code: B

- This **plan** features:
— Three bedrooms
— Two **full** baths

- A convenient one-level design with **an** open floor plan between the Kitchen, Breakfast Area and Great Room

- A vaulted ceiling and a large cozy fireplace in the Great Room

- A well-equipped Kitchen using a peninsula counter as an eating bar

- A Master Suite with a luxurious Master Bath

- This home is designed with slab, **and** crawlspace foundation options

MAIN FLOOR — 1,680 SQ. FT.
GARAGE — 538 SQ. FT.

TOTAL LIVING AREA:
1,680 SQ. FT.

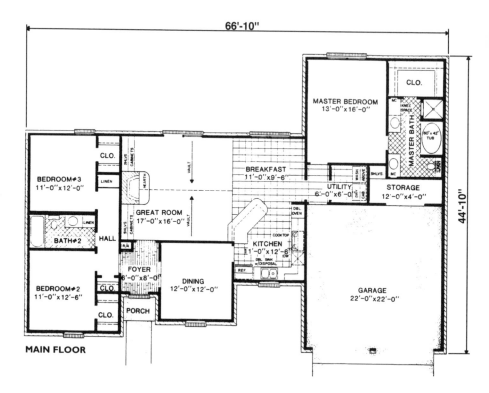

MAIN FLOOR

To order your Blueprints, call 1-800-235-5700

Split-Bedroom Floor Plan

Price Code: A

■ This plan features:

— Three bedrooms

— Two full baths

■ A split-Bedroom floor plan gives the Master Bedroom ultimate privacy

■ The Patio is accessed from the Dining Room and expands dining to the outdoors

■ This home is designed with slab and crawlspace foundation options

MAIN FLOOR — 1,234 SQ. FT.
GARAGE — 523 SQ. FT.

TOTAL LIVING AREA:
1,243 SQ. FT.

MAIN FLOOR

PATIO

52'

41'

MASTER SUITE
12 × 15

BATH

KITCHEN
10 × 11

DINING
10 × 11

BEDRM
11 × 11

DRY   REFG
D/W

WASH

STOR   RNG

SNACK BAR

CLOS

LIN

BATH

CLOS

STORAGE   W   CLOSET

A/C

GREAT RM
15 × 17

FAN

F/P

CLOS

HALL

VAULT   10' CEILING   VAULT

GARAGE
21 × 22

PORCH

BEDRM
11 × 11

A Traditional Ranch

Price Code: C

- This plan features:
— Three bedrooms
— Two full and one half baths
- The two-car Garage offers the option of a third bay or extra storage space
- Columns and a lowered soffit define the separation of Kitchen from Living Room
- This home is designed with a basement foundation

MAIN FLOOR — 1,859 SQ. FT.
GARAGE — 750 SQ. FT.

TOTAL LIVING AREA:
1,859 SQ. FT.

WIDTH 69'-8"
DEPTH 43'-0"

STOR. 11'8" X 20'8"
KIT. 10'0" X 12'0"
NK. 9'8" X 10'0"
LIV. VAULTED CEILING 15'0" X 17'8"
M.B.R. 13'8" X 16'8"
DIN. 10'8" X 12'0"
E. VAULTED CEILING
3 CAR GAR. 23'8" X 21'6"
BR.#3 12'8" X 11'0"
BR.#2 12'0" X 11'4"
LINEN

MAIN FLOOR

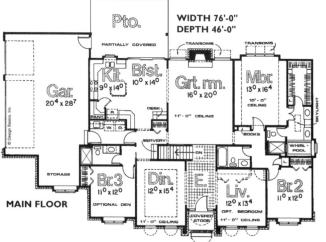

Appealing Brick Elevation

Price Code: D

- This plan features:
— Three bedrooms
— Two full and one three-quarter baths
- Formal Living and Dining Room flanking the Entry
- Impressive Great Room topped by an 11-foot ceiling
- Awning windows framing the raised hearth fireplace
- Attractive Kitchen/Dinette Area including an island, desk, wrapping counters, a walk-in Pantry, and access to the covered Patio
- Pampering Master Suite with a skylight dressing area, a walk-in closet, double vanity, a whirlpool tub, and a decorative plant shelf
- This home is designed with a basement foundation
- Alternate foundation options available at an additional charge. Please call 1-800-235-5700 for more information.

MAIN FLOOR — 2,172 SQ. FT.
GARAGE — 680 SQ. FT.

TOTAL LIVING AREA:
2,172 SQ. FT.

Pto. PARTIALLY COVERED
WIDTH 76'-0"
DEPTH 46'-0"
TRANSOMS
Gar. 20⁴ x 28⁷
Kit. 9⁰ x 14⁰
Bfst. 10⁰ x 14⁰
Grt. rm. 16⁰ x 20⁰ 11'-0" CEILING
Mbr. 13⁰ x 16⁴ 10'-0" CEILING
DESK
PANT.
SERVERY
SKYLIGHT
BOOKS
WHIRL-POOL
STORAGE
Br.3 11⁰ x 12⁰ OPTIONAL DEN
Din. 12⁰ x 15⁴ 11'-0" CEILING
E.
Liv. 12⁰ x 13⁴ OPT. BEDROOM 11'-0" CEILING
Br. 2 11⁰ x 12⁰
COVERED STOOP

MAIN FLOOR

To order your Blueprints, call 1-800-235-5700

MAIN FLOOR

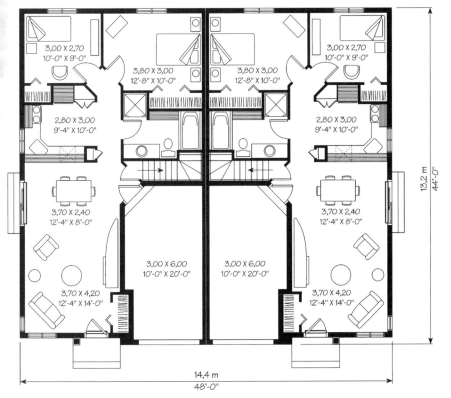

3,00 X 2,70
10'-0" X 9'-0"

3,80 X 3,00
12'-8" X 10'-0"

3,80 X 3,00
12'-8" X 10'-0"

3,00 X 2,70
10'-0" X 9'-0"

2,80 X 3,00
9'-4" X 10'-0"

2,80 X 3,00
9'-4" X 10'-0"

3,70 X 2,40
12'-4" X 8'-0"

3,70 X 2,40
12'-4" X 8'-0"

3,00 X 6,00
10'-0" X 20'-0"

3,00 X 6,00
10'-0" X 20'-0"

3,70 X 4,20
12'-4" X 14'-0"

3,70 X 4,20
12'-4" X 14'-0"

13,2 m
44'-0"

14,4 m
48'-0"

One-Floor Duplex

Price Code: A

■ This plan features:

— Two bedrooms

— One full bath

■ The Living and Dining Rooms flow
together, making a great open space

■ A sliding door off the Dining Room
provides light and access to the side
and rear yards

■ The L-shaped Kitchen boasts an
efficient use of space

■ This home is designed with a basement
foundation

MAIN FLOOR — 834 SQ. FT.
GARAGE — 208 SQ. FT.

TOTAL LIVING AREA:
834 SQ. FT.

Easy Maintenance

Price Code: A

■ This plan features:

— Two bedrooms

— Two three-quarter baths

■ Abundant glass and a wraparound Deck to enjoy the outdoors

■ A tiled entrance into a large Great Room with a fieldstone fireplace and Dining Area under a sloped ceiling

■ A compact tiled Kitchen open to Great Room and adjacent to the Utility Area

■ This home is designed with a crawlspace foundation

MAIN FLOOR — 786 SQ. FT.
DECK — 580 SQ. FT.

TOTAL LIVING AREA:
786 SQ. FT.

MAIN FLOOR

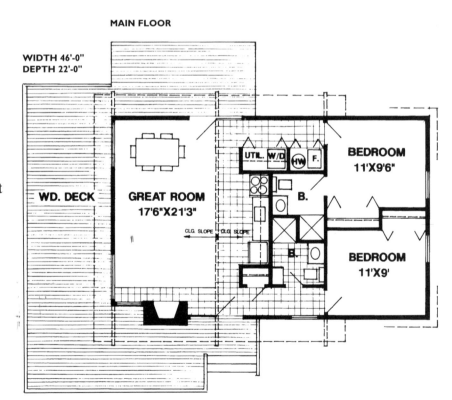

WIDTH 46'-0"
DEPTH 22'-0"

WD. DECK

GREAT ROOM
17'6"X21'3"

CLG. SLOPE   CLG. SLOPE

UTIL. | W/D | HW | F.

B.

B.

BEDROOM
11'X9'6"

BEDROOM
11'X9'

To order your Blueprints, call 1-800-235-5700

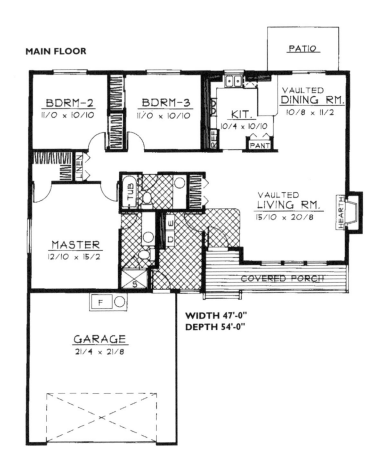

MAIN FLOOR

PATIO

BDRM-2
11/0 x 10/10

BDRM-3
11/0 x 10/10

KIT.
10/4 x 10/10

VAULTED
DINING RM.
10/8 x 11/2

REF

PANT

LINEN

TUB

VAULTED
LIVING RM.
15/10 x 20/8

HEARTH

MASTER
12/10 x 15/2

D E

S

COVERED PORCH

F

WIDTH 47'-0"
DEPTH 54'-0"

GARAGE
21/4 x 21/8

An Affordable, Stylish Floor Plan

Price Code: A

■ This plan features:

— Three bedrooms

— One full and one three quarter baths

■ A Covered Porch Entry

■ An old-fashioned hearth fireplace in the vaulted ceiling Living Room

■ A Kitchen with a handy U-shaped counter that is accessible from the Dining Room

■ A Master Bedroom with a large walk-in closet and private Bath

■ This home is designed with slab and crawlspace foundation options

MAIN FLOOR — 1,410 SQ. FT.
GARAGE — 484 SQ. FT.

TOTAL LIVING AREA: 1,410 SQ. FT.

Great Starter Home

Price Code: B

■ This plan features:
— Three bedrooms
— One full bath

■ The Foyer offers easy access to the Living Room, the Kitchen and Dining Area, the Bedrooms and the basement

■ Plenty of natural light enters the Living Room, thanks to the tall arch-topped window

■ The L-shaped Kitchen is open to the other living areas, with a pentagon-shaped island dileneating the space

■ The three Bedrooms share a full Bath with corner tub and separte shower

■ This home is designed with a basement foundation

MAIN FLOOR — 1,504 SQ. FT.
GARAGE — 424 SQ. FT.

TOTAL LIVING AREA:
1,504 SQ. FT.

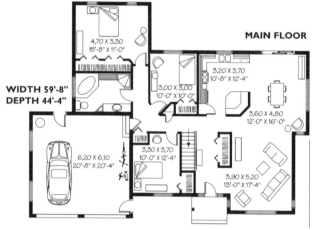

MAIN FLOOR

WIDTH 59'-8"
DEPTH 44'-4"

English Country Elegance

Price Code: I

■ This plan features:
— Four bedrooms
— Three full and one half baths

■ This spectacular Master Suite will provide hours of rest, relaxation, and luxury

■ The fourth Bedroom, with private Bath, is great for overnight guests

■ Entertaining in the cathedral-ceiling Great Room with stone fireplace and impressive built-ins will impress friends

■ Take your breakfast in the window-walled Breakfast Area or more formally in the Dining Room

■ The classic three-car Garage gives you all the extra space you need

■ This home was designed with a slab foundation

MAIN FLOOR — 3,262 SQ. FT
GARAGE — 662 SQ. FT
PORCH — 285 SQ. FT
DECK — 172 SQ. FT

TOTAL LIVING AREA:
3,262 SQ. FT.

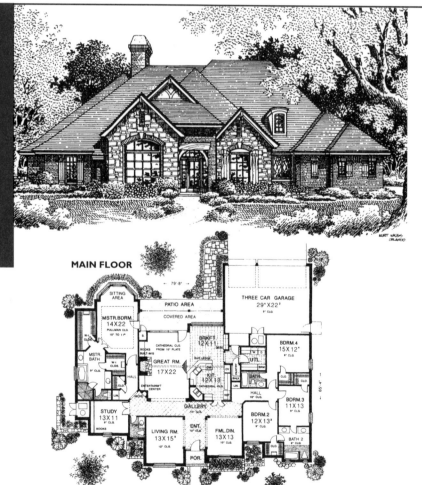

MAIN FLOOR

To order your Blueprints, call 1-800-235-5700

MAIN FLOOR

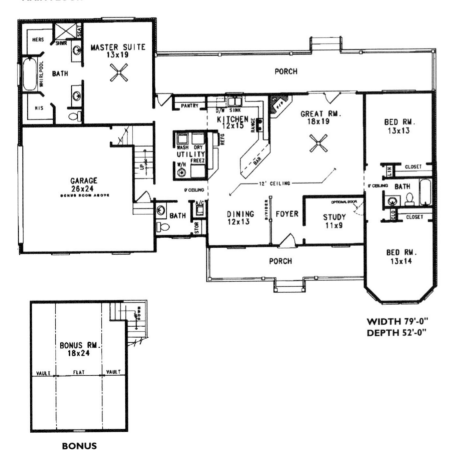

WIDTH 79'-0"
DEPTH 52'-0"

BONUS

Porches Expands Living Space

Price Code: D

■ This plan features:

— Three bedrooms

— Two full and one half baths

■ Porches on the front and the rear of this home expand the living space to the outdoors

■ The spacious Great Room is enhanced by a 12-foot ceiling and a fireplace

■ The well-appointed Kitchen has an extended counter/eating bar

■ The Master Suite is enhanced by double walk-in closets

■ This home is designed with slab and crawlspace foundation options

MAIN FLOOR — 2,089 SQ. FT.
BONUS ROOM — 497 SQ. FT.
GARAGE — 541 SQ. FT.

TOTAL LIVING AREA:
2,089 SQ. FT.

PLAN NO. 97857

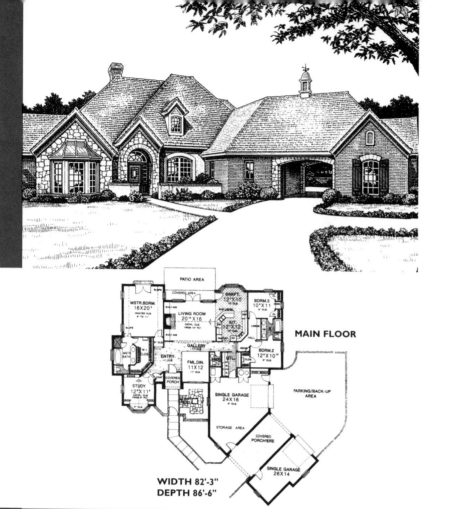

Timeless Country Elegance

Price Code: E

- This plan features:
  — Three bedrooms
  — Two full and one half bath
- A deep Porchiere leads to separate one-car Garages
- The walled Courtyard greets visitors
- A secluded shelf-lined Study offers peaceful reading enjoyment
- Stretching from one side to the other, a long Gallery connects all
- The two children's Bedrooms are connected by a double-vanity Bath
- For shady relaxation, a covered area joins the Patio and Living Room
- This home is designed with a slab foundation

MAIN FLOOR — 2,332 SQ. FT.
GARAGE — 620 SQ. FT.

TOTAL LIVING AREA:
2,332 SQ. FT

MAIN FLOOR

WIDTH 82'-3"
DEPTH 86'-6"

PLAN NO. 82011

Garage Storage

Price Code: B

- This plan features:
  — Three bedrooms
  — Two full baths
- At the heart of the home, the Kitchen opens to a DiningRoom/Hearth Room with a fireplace
- A sloped ceiling and a fireplace enhance the Great Room, located next to the Foyer
- Glass blocks decorate the Master Bath
- This home is designed with basement, slab and crawlspace foundation options

MAIN FLOOR — 1,654 SQ. FT.
GARAGE — 400 SQ. FT.

TOTAL LIVING AREA:
1,654 SQ. FT.

MAIN FLOOR

To order your Blueprints, call 1-800-235-5700

Multiple Gables and a Cozy Front Porch

Price Code: B

■ This plan features:

— Three bedrooms

— Two full baths

■ The Foyer leads to a Great Room capped by a sloped ceiling

■ The Dining Area includes double hung windows

■ A Kitchen providing an abundance of counter space with a Breakfast Bar

■ A Master Bedroom Suite including a walk-in closet and private Bath

■ This home is designed with a basement foundation

MAIN FLOOR — 1,508 SQ. FT.
BASEMENT — 1,439 SQ. FT.
GARAGE — 440 SQ. FT.

TOTAL LIVING AREA:
1,508 SQ. FT.

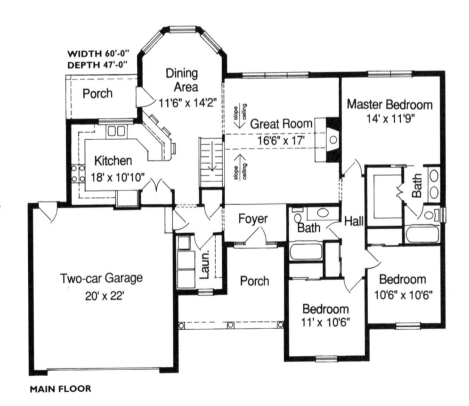

WIDTH 60'-0"
DEPTH 47'-0"

Porch

Dining Area
11'6" x 14'2"

slope ceiling

Great Room
16'6" x 17'

slope ceiling

Master Bedroom
14' x 11'9"

Kitchen
18' x 10'10"

Bath

Foyer

Bath

Hall

Two-car Garage
20' x 22'

Laun.

Porch

Bedroom
10'6" x 10'6"

Bedroom
11' x 10'6"

MAIN FLOOR

121

Classic Spanish Elegance

Price Code: I

■ This plan features:
— Five bedrooms
— Four full baths
■ The unique shapes of this home's rooms give it artistic appeal
■ The Master Bedroom features a window-lined Sitting Area
■ The heavy-traffic areas (Foyer, Kitchen, Breakfast Nook, halls, and Baths) are tiled for easy cleaning
■ A summer Kitchen is ideal for preparing meals to enjoy on the covered Patio
■ This home is designed with a slab foundation

MAIN FLOOR — 3,434 SQ. FT.
BONUS ROOM — 512 SQ. FT.
GARAGE — 814 SQ. FT.

TOTAL LIVING AREA:
3,434 SQ. FT.

WIDTH 82'-4"
DEPTH 83'-8"

MAIN FLOOR

BONUS

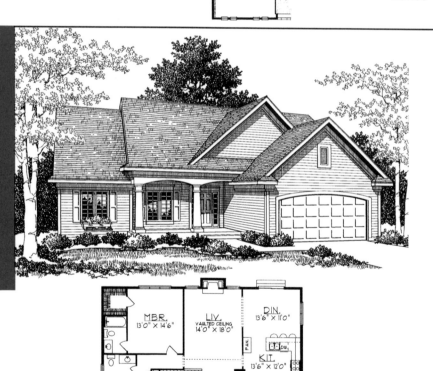

Tall Ceilings

Price Code: B

■ This plan features:
— Three bedrooms
— Two full baths
■ The vaulted ceiling and open layout of the Living Room add drama to the home
■ The Garage storage alcove provides room for sports or lawn equipment
■ One of the secondary Bedrooms has a more than 10-foot-high ceiling
■ This home is designed with a basement foundation

MAIN FLOOR — 1,537 SQ. FT.

TOTAL LIVING AREA:
1,537 SQ. FT.

MAIN FLOOR

WIDTH 52'-0"
DEPTH 50'-0"

To order your Blueprints, call 1-800-235-5700

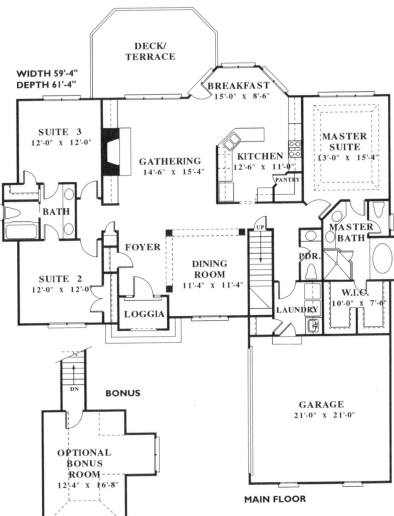

WIDTH 59'-4"
DEPTH 61'-4"

DECK/ TERRACE

BREAKFAST
15'-0" x 8'-6"

SUITE 3
12'-0" x 12'-0"

GATHERING
14'-6" x 15'-4"

KITCHEN
12'-6" x 11'-0"

MASTER SUITE
13'-0" x 15'-4"

PANTRY

BATH

FOYER

DINING ROOM
11'-4" x 11'-4"

UP

MASTER BATH

PDR.

SUITE 2
12'-0" x 12'-0"

LOGGIA

LAUNDRY

W.I.C.
10'-0" x 7'-6"

BONUS

DN

GARAGE
21'-0" x 21'-0"

OPTIONAL BONUS ROOM
12'-4" x 16'-8"

MAIN FLOOR

Step-Saving Floor Plan

Price Code: C

■ This plan features:

— Three bedrooms

— Two full and one half baths

■ Recessed entrance leads into Foyer, Dining Room defined by columns, and Gathering Room beyond

■ Expansive Gathering Room with an inviting fireplace, opens to Deck/Terrace and Breakfast/ Kitchen Area for comfortable gatherings

■ This home is designed with basement and crawlspace foundation options

MAIN FLOOR — 1,950 SQ. FT.
BASEMENT — 1,287 SQ. FT.
GARAGE — 466 SQ. FT.
BONUS — 255 SQ. FT.

TOTAL LIVING AREA:
1,950 SQ. FT.

Expansive Living Room

Price Code: A

■ This plan features:

— Three bedrooms

— Two full baths

■ Vaulted ceiling crowns spacious Living Room highlighted by a fireplace

■ Walk-in closet and a private five-piece Bath topped by a vaulted ceiling in the Master Bedroom

■ This home is designed with basement, slab, and crawlspace foundation options

MAIN FLOOR — 1,346 SQ. FT.
GARAGE — 395 SQ. FT.
BASEMENT — 1,358 SQ. FT.

TOTAL LIVING AREA:
1,346 SQ. FT.

MAIN FLOOR

© Frank Betz Associates, Inc.

To order your Blueprints, call 1-800-235-5700

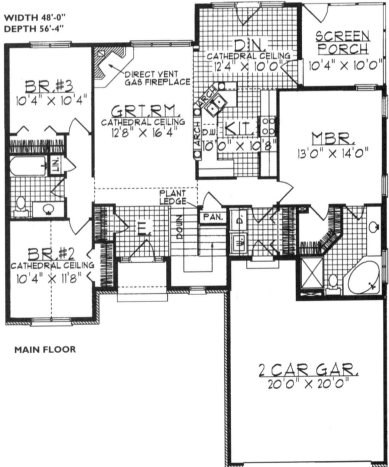

WIDTH 48'-0"
DEPTH 56'-4"

BR. #3
10'4" X 10'4"

DIRECT VENT
GAS FIREPLACE

DIN.
CATHEDRAL CEILING
12'4" X 10'0"

SCREEN
PORCH
10'4" X 10'0"

GRT. RM.
CATHEDRAL CEILING
12'8" X 16'4"

KIT.
10'0" X 10'8"

MBR.
13'0" X 14'0"

PLANT
LEDGE

PAN.

BR. #2
CATHEDRAL CEILING
10'4" X 11'8"

DOWN

LIN.

2 CAR GAR.
20'0" X 20'0"

MAIN FLOOR

Brick Details Add Class

Price Code: A

■ This plan features:

— Three bedrooms

— Two full baths

■ Keystone entrance leads into easy-care, tile Entry

■ Expansive Great Room has a cathedral ceiling

■ Hub Kitchen is accented by arches and columns

■ Adjoining Dining Area with large windows and outdoor access

■ Master Bedroom suite has a plush Bath

■ This home is designed with a basement foundation

MAIN FLOOR — 1,472 SQ. FT.
BASEMENT — 1,472 SQ. FT.
GARAGE — 424 SQ. FT.

TOTAL LIVING AREA:
1,472 SQ. FT.

Charming and Stylish

Price Code: D

■ This plan features:

— Three bedrooms

— Two full baths

■ The front Entry flows into a spacious Great Room with a fireplace and view of a charming back Porch

■ The efficient Kitchen has a center-island cook top and sunny Breakfast Nook

■ The Master Bedroom and the Dining Room both have raised ceilings

■ This plan features several built-ins, such as window seats, bookcases, and even a computer niche in the Kitchen

■ This home is designed with a slab foundation

MAIN FLOOR — 2,028 SQ. FT.
GARAGE — 442 SQ. FT.

TOTAL LIVING AREA:
2,028 SQ. FT.

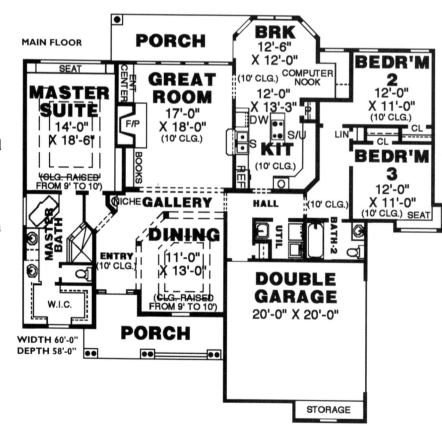

MAIN FLOOR

PORCH

BRK
12'-6"
X 12'-0"
(10' CLG.)

BEDR'M
2
12'-0"
X 11'-0"
(10' CLG.)

SEAT

GREAT
ROOM
17'-0"
X 18'-0"
(10' CLG.)

COMPUTER
NOOK

12'-0"
X 13'-3"

MASTER
SUITE
14'-0"
X 18'-6"

F/P

DW

S/U

KIT
(10' CLG.)

LIN

CL

CL

BEDR'M
3
12'-0"
X 11'-0"
(10' CLG.) SEAT

(CLG. RAISED
FROM 9' TO 10')

BOOKS

REF

NICHE GALLERY

HALL

(10' CLG.)

MASTER
BATH

ENTRY
(10' CLG.)

DINING
11'-0"
X 13'-0"

UTIL

BATH-2

W.I.C.

(CLG. RAISED
FROM 9' TO 10')

DOUBLE
GARAGE
20'-0" X 20'-0"

WIDTH 60'-0"
DEPTH 58'-0"

PORCH

STORAGE

To order your Blueprints, call 1-800-235-5700

A Versatile Back Porch

Price Code: A

■ This plan features:

— Three bedrooms

— Two full baths

■ Clever open bar connects the Kitchen and Great Room

■ One wall of the Breakfast Room contains a built-in computer desk

■ A large bay window creates a light-filled Dining Room

■ The Bedroom near the front entrance could be used as a Study or Playroom

■ A glass-block window lights the Master Bath's whirlpool tub

■ The Master Suite features double walk-in closets

■ This home is designed with slab and crawlspace foundation options

MAIN FLOOR — 1,485 SQ. FT.
GARAGE — 415 SQ. FT.

TOTAL LIVING AREA:
1,485 SQ. FT.

© Michael E. Nelson

Rear Elevation

WIDTH 51'-6"
DEPTH 49'-10"

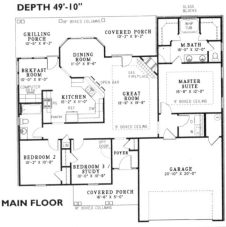

MAIN FLOOR

Master Retreat Welcomes You Home

Price Code: A

■ This plan features:

— Three bedrooms

— Two full baths

■ Foyer opens into an huge Living Room with a fireplace, a sloped ceiling, and Deck access

■ Efficient Kitchen with a Pantry, serving counter, Dining Area, Laundry closet, and Garage Entry

■ Corner Master Bedroom offers a walk-in closet and pampering Bath with a raised tub

■ Two more Bedrooms, one with a Den option, share a full Bath

■ This home is designed with basement, slab, and crawlspace foundation options

MAIN FLOOR — 1,486 SQ. FT.
GARAGE — 462 SQ. FT.

TOTAL LIVING AREA:
1,486 SQ. FT.

MAIN FLOOR

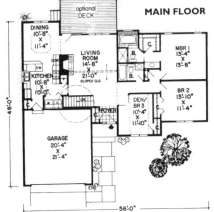

OPTIONAL
CRAWLSPACE/SLAB

To order your Blueprints, call 1-800-235-5700

Quiet Den or Office

Price Code: C

■ This plan features:

— Three bedrooms

— Two full baths

■ The combined Kitchen and Dining Room open into an expansive Great Room with backyard vistas

■ The Garage contains an extra bay that is perfect for a workshop or third vehicle

■ One of the secondary Bedrooms has a walk-in closet

■ This home is designed with a crawlspace foundation

MAIN FLOOR — 1,852 SQ. FT.
GARAGE — 757 SQ. FT.

TOTAL LIVING AREA:
1,852 SQ. FT.

MAIN FLOOR

MASTER
16/2 X 14/0
(9' CLG.)

BUILT-IN

GREAT RM.
17/6 X 20/6
(12'-4" CLG.)

DINING
11/6 X 13/0
(9' CLG.)

8/6 X 15/0

SHOP /
3RD CAR
12/6 X 19/6

PAN.

NICHE

DEN
11/0 X 10/0
(9' CLG.)

BR. 2
11/0 X 12/6
(9' CLG.)

LIN.

BR. 3
11/2 X 12/0
(9' CLG.)

GARAGE
21/0 X 22/6

©Alan Mascord Design Associates, Inc.

WIDTH 70'-0"
DEPTH 45'-0"

Outstanding Elevation

Price Code: F

- This plan features:
  - Three bedrooms
  - One full, two three-quarter, and one half baths
- Grand double door entrance into Foyer and formal Dining Room and Grand Room defined by columns
- Efficient Kitchen with Pantry and cooktop island easily serves Breakfast Area, Deck and Keeping Den
- This home is designed with a crawlspace foundation

MAIN FLOOR — 2,677 SQ. FT.
GARAGE — 543 SQ. FT.
BONUS — 319 SQ. FT.

TOTAL LIVING AREA:
2,677 SQ. FT.

WIDTH 63'-10"
DEPTH 80'-4"

MAIN FLOOR

Grow Into This Home

Price Code: D

- This plan features:
  - Two bedrooms
  - Two full and one half baths
- Extend the Kitchen/Dining Area with an optional bay window for backyard views
- A complete Master Suite includes an option for soaking tub and linen closet
- 12-foot ceilings add drama to the spacious Family Room
- Create inviting appeal with the luxurious Entry
- This home is designed with basement, slab, and crawlspace foundation options

MAIN FLOOR — 2,142 SQ. FT.
GARAGE — 574 SQ. FT.

TOTAL LIVING AREA:
2,142 SQ. FT.

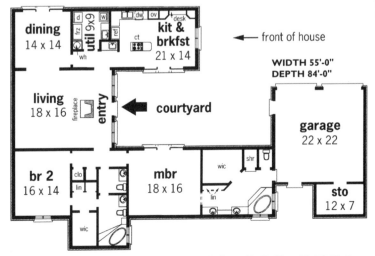

MAIN FLOOR

WIDTH 55'-0"
DEPTH 84'-0"

← front of house

dining 14 x 14
kit & brkfst 21 x 14
living 18 x 16
entry
courtyard
garage 22 x 22
br 2 16 x 14
mbr 18 x 16
sto 12 x 7

To order your Blueprints, call 1-800-235-5700

Moderate Ranch

Price Code: C

■ This plan features:

— Three bedrooms

— Two full baths

■ A large Great Room with a vaulted ceiling and a stone fireplace with bookshelves on either side

■ A spacious Kitchen, with ample cabinet space, conveniently located next to the large Dining Room

■ A Master Suite with a private Bath highlighted by a garden tub, double-vanity, and walk-in closet

■ This home is designed with basement, slab, and crawlspace foundation options

MAIN FLOOR — 1,811 SQ. FT.
BASEMENT — 1,811 SQ. FT.
GARAGE — 484 SQ. FT.

TOTAL LIVING AREA:
1,811 SQ. FT.

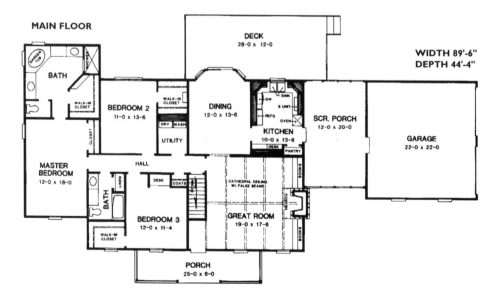

To order your Blueprints, call 1-800-235-5700

MAIN FLOOR

PORCH

DINING
11/2 X 12/8
(9' CLG.)

VAULTED
MASTER
12/8 X 15/2

SHELVES

BUILT-INS

VAULTED
GREAT RM.
16/8 X 17/0

11/4 X 12/10

W. D

▲
48'
▼

MEDIA

LIN. LIN.

REF.

P.

FOYER
(10' CLG.)

BR. 3/
DEN
10/6 X 11/4
(9' CLG.)

GARAGE
20/6 X 21/0

BR. 2
11/0 X 10/0
(9' CLG.)

© Alan Mascord Design Associates, Inc.

PORCH

◄ 50' ►

Shapes and Textures add Appeal

Price Code: B

■ This plan features:

— Two bedrooms

— Two full and one half baths

■ The Master Suite provides a private retreat to homeowners

■ The vaulted Great Room has a corner fireplace and built-in media center

■ Arch-top windows offer a view to the rear Porch from the Great Room

■ The Kitchen includes ample work and storage space

■ This home is designed with a crawlspace foundation

MAIN FLOOR — 1,580 SQ. FT.
GARAGE — 452 SQ. FT.

TOTAL LIVING AREA:
1,580 SQ. FT.

A Must See Design

Price Code: D

■ This plan features:
— Three bedrooms
— Two full baths
■ Attractive, arched entrance leads into Great Room with a wall of windows and an expansive cathedral ceiling above a cozy fireplace
■ Convenient Kitchen easily accesses Nook and Dining Areas, Laundry and Garage
■ Corner Master Bedroom is enhanced by two large, walk-in closets, a cathedral ceiling and a double vanity Bath
■ This home is designed with a basement foundation

MAIN FLOOR — 2,229 SQ. FT.
BASEMENT — 2,229 SQ. FT.
GARAGE — 551 SQ. FT.

TOTAL LIVING AREA:
2,229 SQ. FT.

MAIN FLOOR

Simply Irresistible

Price Code: B

■ This plan features:
— Three bedrooms
— Two full baths
■ An 11-foot ceiling in the Entry welcomes visitors
■ A serving bar between Kitchen and Family Room is great for entertaining
■ The luxurious Master Suite includes deluxe Bath and Sitting Area among its amenities
■ This home was designed with a slab foundation

MAIN FLOOR — 1,681 SQ. FT.
GARAGE — 427 SQ. FT.

TOTAL LIVING AREA:
1,681 SQ. FT.

WIDTH 55'-8"
DEPTH 53'-2"

MAIN FLOOR

To order your Blueprints, call 1-800-235-5700

Varied Roof Heights Create Interesting Lines

Price Code: B

■ This plan features:

— Three bedrooms

— Two full and one half baths

■ A spacious Family Room with a heat-circulating fireplace

■ A large Kitchen with a cooktop island, opening into the Dinette Bay

■ A Master Suite with his-n-her closets and a private Master Bath

■ Formal Dining and Living Rooms, flow into each other for easy entertaining

■ This home is designed with basement and slab foundation options

MAIN FLOOR — 1,613 SQ. FT.
BASEMENT — 1,060 SQ. FT.
GARAGE — 461 SQ. FT.

TOTAL LIVING AREA:
1,613 SQ. FT.

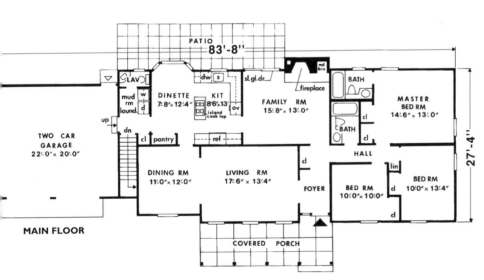

Quaint and Cozy

Price Code: B

■ This plan features:

— Three bedrooms

— Two full baths

■ This home has a split-Bedroom design

■ Columns set the formal Dining Room

■ The open Kitchen, eating Nook, and Dining Room are perfect for entertaining

■ A rear Porch adds living space

■ This home is designed with a crawlspace foundation

MAIN FLOOR — 1,699 SQ. FT.

TOTAL LIVING AREA:
1,699 SQ. FT.

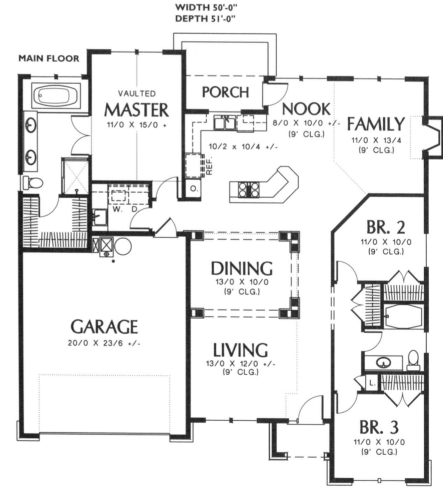

WIDTH 50'-0"
DEPTH 51'-0"

MAIN FLOOR

VAULTED
MASTER
11/0 X 15/0 +

PORCH

NOOK
8/0 X 10/0 +/-
(9' CLG.)

FAMILY
11/0 X 13/4
(9' CLG.)

10/2 x 10/4 +/-

REF.

W. D.

BR. 2
11/0 X 10/0
(9' CLG.)

GARAGE
20/0 X 23/6 +/-

DINING
13/0 X 10/0
(9' CLG.)

LIVING
13/0 X 12/0 +/-
(9' CLG.)

BR. 3
11/0 X 10/0
(9' CLG.)

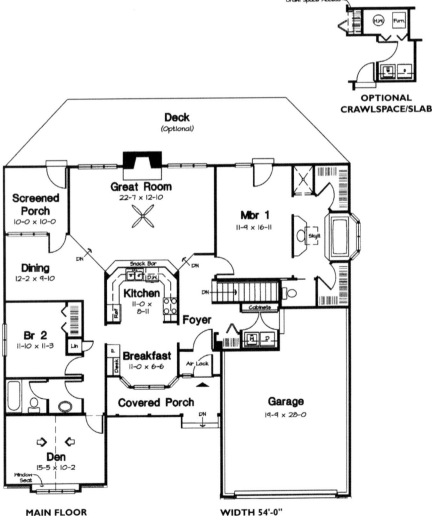

Crawl Space Access

OPTIONAL CRAWLSPACE/SLAB

Deck
(Optional)

Screened Porch
10-0 x 10-0

Great Room
22-7 x 12-10

Mbr 1
11-9 x 16-11

Skylit

Dining
12-2 x 9-10

Snack Bar

Kitchen
11-0 x 8-11

DN

Ref

Foyer

Cabinets

Br 2
11-10 x 11-3

Lin

Breakfast
11-0 x 6-6

Air Lock

P

P

Covered Porch

DN

Garage
19-9 x 28-0

Den
15-5 x 10-2

Window Seat

MAIN FLOOR

WIDTH 54'-0"
DEPTH 50'-0"

Energy Efficient Air-Lock Entry

Price Code: C

■ This plan features:

— Two bedrooms

— Two full baths

■ The attractive Covered Porch highlights the curb appeal of this charming home

■ A Screened Porch, accessed from the Dining Room, extends the living space to the outdoors

■ The Master Bath features a garden tub, separate shower, double walk-in closets, and a skylight

■ This home is designed with crawlspace, slab, and combo basement/crawlspace foundation options

MAIN FLOOR — 1,771 SQ. FT.
BASEMENT — 1,194 SQ. FT.
GARAGE — 517 SQ. FT.

TOTAL LIVING AREA:
1,771 SQ. FT.

Traditional Ranch

Price Code: E

■ This plan features:

— Three bedrooms

— Two full baths

■ A tray ceiling over Master Suite which is equipped with his and her walk-in closets and a private Master Bath with a cathedral ceiling

■ A formal Living Room with a cathedral ceiling

■ A decorative tray ceiling in the elegant formal Dining Room

■ A spacious Family Room with a vaulted ceiling and a fireplace

■ A modern, well-appointed Kitchen with snack bar and bayed Breakfast Area

■ This home is designed with a basement foundation

MAIN FLOOR — 2,275 SQ. FT.
BASEMENT — 2,207 SQ. FT.
GARAGE — 512 SQ. FT.

TOTAL LIVING AREA:
2,275 SQ. FT.

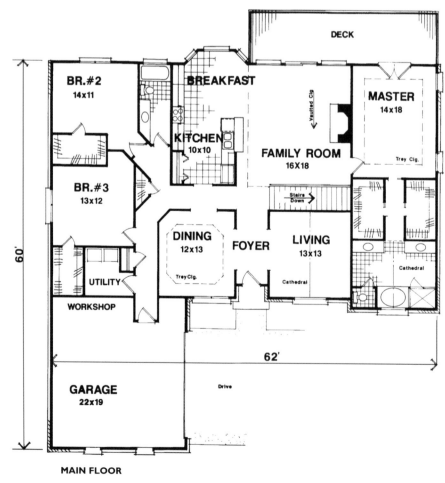

DECK

BR. #2
14x11

BREAKFAST

MASTER
14x18

Vaulted Clg

Trey Clg.

KITCHEN
10x10

FAMILY ROOM
16X18

BR. #3
13x12

Stairs Down

60'

DINING
12x13

FOYER

LIVING
13x13

Cathedral

Trey Clg.

Cathedral

UTILITY

WORKSHOP

62'

GARAGE
22x19

Drive

MAIN FLOOR

To order your Blueprints, call 1-800-235-5700

Country Flair

Price Code: A

■ This plan features:
— Three bedrooms
— Two full baths

■ An inviting front Porch leads into a tiled Entry and Great Room with focal point fireplace

■ Open layout of Great Room, Dining Area, Wood Deck and Kitchen easily accommodates a busy family

■ Master Bedroom set in a quiet corner, offers a huge walk-in closet and double vanity Bath

■ Two additional Bedrooms, one an optional Den, share a full hall Bath

■ This home is designed with a basement foundation

MAIN FLOOR — 1,461 SQ. FT.
BASEMENT — 1,461 SQ. FT.
GARAGE — 458 SQ. FT.

TOTAL LIVING AREA:
1,461 SQ. FT.

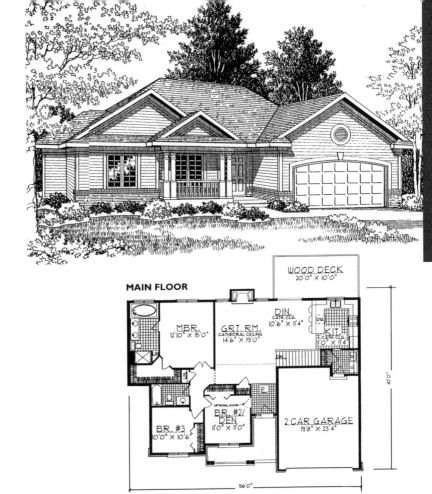

MAIN FLOOR

WOOD DECK 20'0" X 10'0"

DIN. CATH. CLG. 10'6" X 11'4"

KIT. 1-CAR CLG. 10'0" X 11'4"

MBR. 12'10" X 15'0"

GRT. RM. CATHEDRAL CEILING 14'6" X 19'0"

2 CAR GARAGE 19'8" X 23'4"

BR. #2/ DEN 11'0" X 11'0"

BR. #3 10'0" X 10'6"

OPTIONAL DOOR

45'0"

56'0"

Grow Into This Home

Price Code: A

■ This plan features:
— Three bedrooms
— Two full baths

■ Extend the Kitchen/Dining Area with an optional bay window for backyard views

■ A complete Master Suite includes an option for soaking tub and linen closet

■ 12-foot ceilings add drama to the spacious Family Room

■ Create inviting appeal with the luxurious Entry

■ This home was designed with basement, slab, and crawlspace foudation options

MAIN FLOOR — 1,296 SQ. FT.
GARAGE — 380 SQ. FT.
BASEMENT — 1,336 SQ. FT.

TOTAL LIVING AREA:
1,296 SQ. FT.

OPTIONAL BAY

BEDROOM 2 11x11

DINING

FAMILY ROOM 16x20

KITCHEN 10x10

BEDROOM 3 11x10

12' CEILING

W D

WIDTH 46'-0"
DEPTH 42'-0"

GARAGE 19x20

MASTER BEDROOM 12x14

VLT.

LIN.

MASTER BATH OPTION

MAIN FLOOR

To order your Blueprints, call 1-800-235-5700

Classic Columns

Price Code: C

■ This plan features:

— Three bedrooms

— Two full and one half baths

■ A classic Porch and dormers give this home timeless appeal

■ Columns grace the entrance of the formal Dining Room and the Great Room

■ The Master Suite features a luxurious Bath and generous walk-in closet

■ The Kitchen, with island and built-in computer desk, is an ideal space for cooking and more

■ This home is designed with slab and crawlspace foundation options

MAIN FLOOR — 1,988 SQ. FT.
GARAGE — 598 SQ. FT.

TOTAL LIVING AREA:
1,988 SQ. FT.

MAIN FLOOR

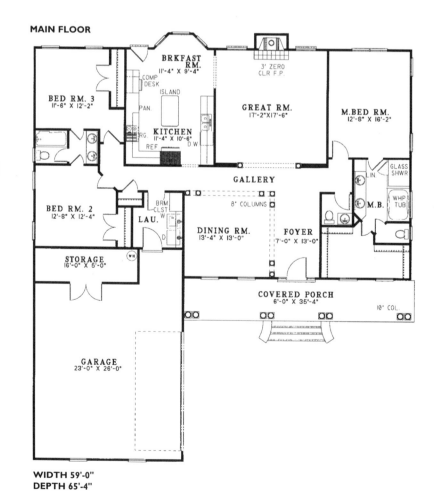

WIDTH 59'-0"
DEPTH 65'-4"

To order your Blueprints, call 1-800-235-5700

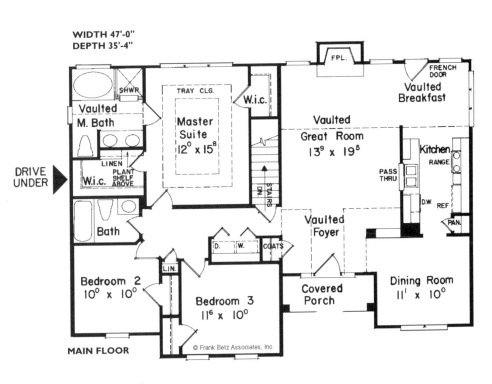

WIDTH 47'-0"
DEPTH 35'-4"

SHWR

Vaulted
M. Bath

TRAY CLG.

W.i.c.

Master
Suite
12⁰ x 15⁸

LINEN

PLANT
SHELF
ABOVE

W.i.c.

DRIVE
UNDER

Bath

Bedroom 2
10⁰ x 10⁰

LIN.

D. W. COATS

Bedroom 3
11⁶ x 10⁰

FPL.

FRENCH
DOOR

Vaulted
Breakfast

Vaulted
Great Room
13⁹ x 19⁵

STAIRS

DN

Kitchen

RANGE

PASS
THRU

D.W. REF

PAN.

Vaulted
Foyer

Covered
Porch

Dining Room
11' x 10⁰

MAIN FLOOR

© Frank Betz Associates, Inc.

Vaulted Ceilings Create Spacious Feelings

Price Code: A

■ This plan features:

— Three bedrooms

— Two full baths

■ Open layout with vaulted ceilings in Foyer, Great Room, and Breakfast Area

■ Kitchen with pass-through and Pantry, efficiently serves bright Breakfast Area, Great Room, and formal Dining Room

■ This home is designed with a basement foundation

MAIN FLOOR — 1,363 SQ. FT.
BASEMENT — 715 SQ. FT.
GARAGE — 677 SQ. FT.

TOTAL LIVING AREA:
1,363 SQ. FT.

To order your Blueprints, call 1-800-235-5700

Compact and Beautiful

Price Code: C

■ This plan features:
— Three bedrooms
— Two full baths
■ Only 30-foot wide, this unique home fits on a narrow lot
■ Even with it's slender design, the home's Master Suite is fully loaded
■ The ample, one and a-half car Garage offers plenty of auxiliary storage space
■ The efficient though complete galley Kitchen anchors the home
■ This home is designed with a slab foundation

MAIN FLOOR — 1,118 SQ. FT.

TOTAL LIVING AREA: 1,118 SQ. FT.

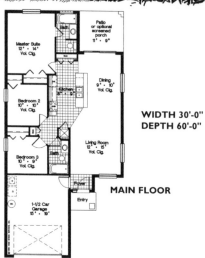

WIDTH 30'-0"
DEPTH 60'-0"

MAIN FLOOR

Open Areas for Entertaining

Price Code: B

■ This plan features:
— Three bedrooms
— Two full baths
■ The Great-Room features a nine-foot-high raised ceiling, a hearth fireplace, and access to the backyard
■ The Kitchen includes a Pantry and is only steps away from both the Laundry and Dining Rooms
■ This home is designed with basement, slab, and crawlspace foundation options

MAIN FLOOR — 1,538 SQ. FT.
GARAGE — 441 SQ. FT.

TOTAL LIVING AREA: 1,538 SQ. FT.

MAIN FLOOR

To order your Blueprints, call 1-800-235-5700

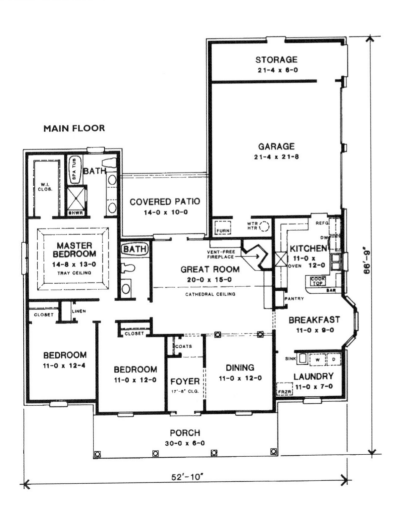

MAIN FLOOR

STORAGE
21-4 x 6-0

GARAGE
21-4 x 21-8

BATH

W.I.
CLOS.

SPA TUB

SHWR

COVERED PATIO
14-0 x 10-0

FURN

WTR
HTR

REFG

DW

KITCHEN
11-0 x
12-0

OVEN

COOK
TOP

BAR

MASTER
BEDROOM
14-8 x 13-0
TRAY CEILING

BATH

VENT-FREE
FIREPLACE

GREAT ROOM
20-0 x 15-0

CATHEDRAL CEILING

PANTRY

CLOSET

LINEN

BREAKFAST
11-0 x 9-0

BEDROOM
11-0 x 12-4

CLOSET

COATS

BEDROOM
11-0 x 12-0

FOYER
17'-8" CLG.

DINING
11-0 x 12-0

SINK

W

D

LAUNDRY
11-0 x 7-0

FRZR

PORCH
30-0 x 6-0

86'-8"

52'-10"

Angled & Vent-Free Fireplace in Great-Room

Price Code: B

■ This plan features:

— Three bedrooms

— Two full baths

■ Dining Room, Breakfast Bay, and and eating bar offer formal and casual dining

■ Garage fitted with Storage Space for golf cart, sports equipment, and lawn tools

■ This home is designed with slab and crawlspace foundation options

MAIN FLOOR — 1,672 SQ. FT.
GARAGE — 650 SQ. FT.

TOTAL LIVING AREA:
1,672 SQ. FT.

Those Fabulous Details

Price Code: E

■ This plan features:

— Three bedrooms

— Two full and one half baths

■ Hub of home is vaulted Family Room with French door

■ Vaulted Breakfast Area expands efficient Kitchen

■ Spacious Master Suite boasts a Sitting Area with fireplace

■ This home is designed with basement and crawlspace foundation options

MAIN FLOOR — 2,311 SQ. FT.
BONUS — 425 SQ. FT.
BASEMENT — 2,311 SQ. FT.
GARAGE — 500 SQ. FT.

TOTAL LIVING AREA:
2,311 SQ. FT.

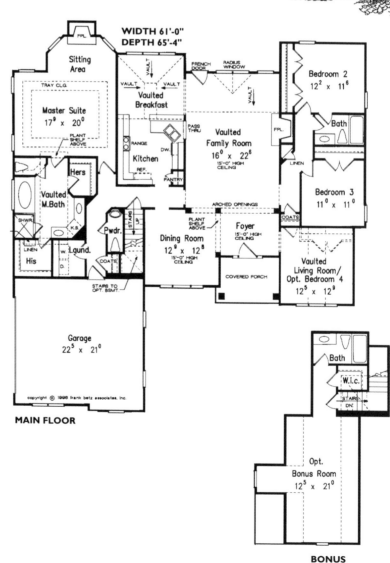

WIDTH 61'-0"
DEPTH 65'-4"

MAIN FLOOR

BONUS

High Ceilings and Arched Windows

Price Code: B

■ This plan features:
— Three bedrooms
— Two full baths
■ Kitchen with a serving bar to the Breakfast Room
■ Tray ceiling in the Master Suite and a vaulted ceiling over the Sitting Room and the Master Bath
■ This home is designed with basement and crawlspace foundation options

MAIN FLOOR — 1,502 SQ. FT.
GARAGE — 448 SQ. FT.
BASEMENT — 1,555 SQ. FT.

TOTAL LIVING AREA:
1,502 SQ. FT.

MAIN FLOOR

WIDTH 51'-0"
DEPTH 50'-6"

OPTIONAL BASEMENT STAIR LOCATION

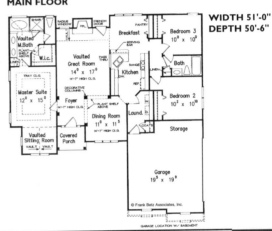

Complete Efficiency

Price Code: A

■ This plan features:
— Three bedrooms
— Two full baths
■ Careful design makes this home "live" much bigger than it really is
■ A vaulted ceiling in the Family Room adds scale and drama
■ The Laundry Room is conveniently placed between Kitchen and Garage
■ A soaking tub, double vanity and vaulted ceiling add to the elegance of the Master Bath
■ The Master Suite includes a large walk-in closet for ample storage
■ This home was designed with slab and crawlspace foundation options

MAIN FLOOR — 1,197 SQ. FT.
GARAGE — 380 SQ. FT.

TOTAL LIVING AREA:
1,197 SQ. FT.

WIDTH 52'-0"
DEPTH 42'-0"

MAIN FLOOR

To order your Blueprints, call 1-800-235-5700

MAIN FLOOR

Elegant Ceiling Treatments

Price Code: B

- This plan features:
  - — Three Bedrooms
  - — Two full baths
- Dining Room defined by columns
- Kitchen highlighted by a peninsula counter/serving bar
- Vaulted ceiling highlighting the Great Room which also includes a fireplace between radius windows
- This home is designed with basement and crawlspace foundation options

FIRST FLOOR — 1,692 SQ. FT.
BONUS ROOM — 358 SQ. FT.
BASEMENT — 1,705 SQ. FT.
GARAGE — 472 SQ. FT.

TOTAL LIVING AREA:
1,692 SQ. FT.

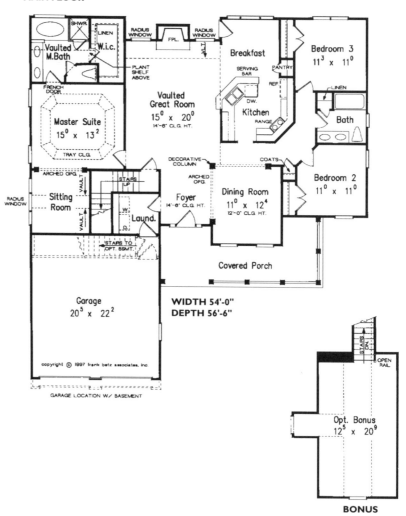

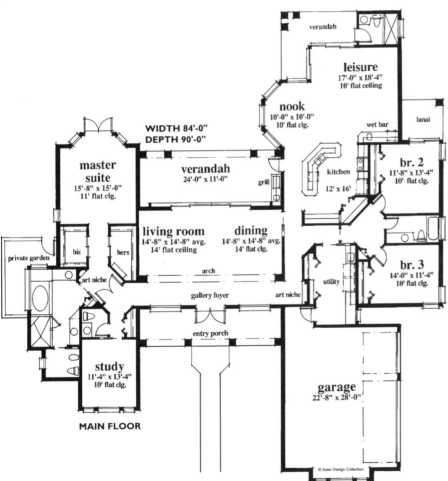

verandah

leisure
17'-0" x 18'-4"
10' flat ceiling

nook
10'-0" x 10'-0"
10' flat clg.

lanai

WIDTH 84'-0"
DEPTH 90'-0"

master
suite
15'-8" x 15'-0"
11' flat clg.

verandah
24'-0" x 11'-0"

grill

wet bar

kitchen
12' x 16'

br. 2
11'-8" x 13'-4"
10' flat clg.

private garden

his   hers

art niche

living room
14'-8" x 14'-8" avg.
14' flat ceiling

dining
14'-8" x 14'-8" avg.
14' flat clg.

arch

gallery foyer

art niche

utility

br. 3
14'-0" x 11'-4"
10' flat clg.

entry porch

study
11'-4" x 13'-4"
10' flat clg.

garage
22'-8" x 28'-0"

MAIN FLOOR

© Sater Design Collection

A Custom Look
Price Code: H

- This plan features:
  — Three bedrooms
  — Two full, one half, and one three-quarter baths

- Exterior highlighted by triple arched glass in Entry Porch

- Triple arches lead into Formal Living and Dining Rooms, Veranda and beyond

- Owners' wing has a Master Suite with glass alcove to rear yard, a lavish Bath, and a Study

- This home is designed with a slab foundation

- Alternate foundation options available at an additional charge. Please call 1-800-235-5700 for more information.

MAIN FLOOR — 2,978 SQ. FT.
GARAGE — 702 SQ. FT.

TOTAL LIVING AREA:
2,978 SQ. FT.

European Styling with a Georgian Flair

Price Code: C

■ This plan features:

— Four bedrooms

— Two full baths

■ Arched windows, quoins, and shutters on the exterior, a columned covered front and a rear Porch

■ Kitchen flows into the informal Eating Area

■ Split-Bedroom plan with Master Suite privately place to the rear

■ This home is designed with slab and crawlspace foundation options

MAIN FLOOR — 1,873 SQ. FT.
GARAGE — 613 SQ. FT.
BONUS — 145 SQ. FT.

TOTAL LIVING AREA:
1,873 SQ. FT.

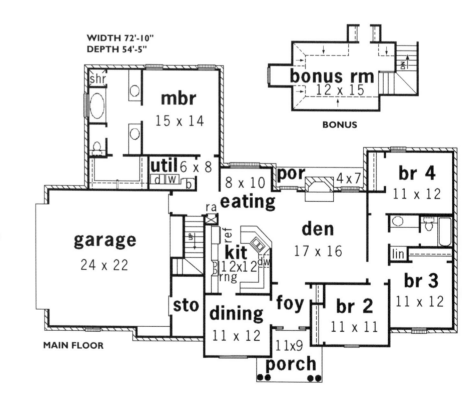

WIDTH 72'-10"
DEPTH 54'-5"

- shr
- mbr 15 x 14
- util 6 x 8 / d w / b
- garage 24 x 22
- eating 8 x 10
- por 4 x 7
- bonus rm 12 x 15
- BONUS
- br 4 11 x 12
- ra
- ref
- kit 12x12 / dw
- rng
- den 17 x 16
- lin
- br 3 11 x 12
- sto
- dining 11 x 12
- foy
- br 2 11 x 11
- 11x9
- porch

MAIN FLOOR

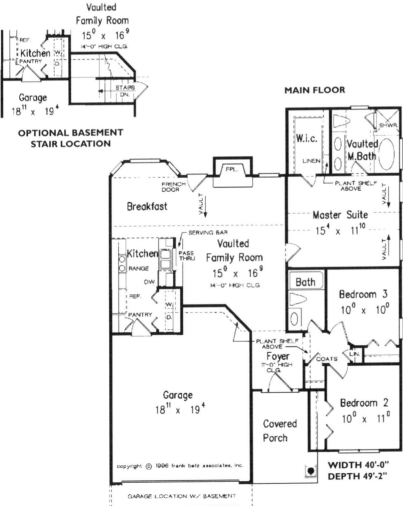

Vaulted
Family Room
15⁰ x 16⁹
14'-0" HIGH CLG.

REF.
Kitchen
PANTRY
W.
D.

Garage
18¹¹ x 19⁴

STAIRS
DN.

**OPTIONAL BASEMENT
STAIR LOCATION**

MAIN FLOOR

W.i.c.
LINEN
SHWR.
Vaulted
M.Bath
PLANT SHELF
ABOVE

Master Suite
15⁴ x 11¹⁰

VAULT

Breakfast

FRENCH
DOOR

FPL.

VAULT

SERVING BAR

Kitchen
RANGE
DW
REF.
PANTRY
W. D.

PASS THRU

Vaulted
Family Room
15⁰ x 16⁹
14'-0" HIGH CLG.

Bath

Bedroom 3
10⁰ x 10⁰

PLANT SHELF
ABOVE

Foyer
11'-0" HIGH
CLG.

COATS

LN.

Garage
18¹¹ x 19⁴

Bedroom 2
10⁰ x 11⁰

Covered
Porch

copyright © 1996 frank betz associates, inc.

WIDTH 40'-0"
DEPTH 49'-2"

GARAGE LOCATION W/ BASEMENT

Charming
Three Bedroom

Price Code: A

■ This plan features:

— Three bedrooms

— Two full baths

■ Covered Porch leads into Foyer
and to the Family Room beyond

■ Efficient Kitchen with Pantry,
Laundry, and pass-through opens
to bright Breakfast Area

■ This home is designed with
basement and crawlspace
foundation options

MAIN FLOOR — 1,222 SQ. FT.
LOWER FLOOR — 1,218 SQ. FT.
GARAGE — 410 SQ. FT.

TOTAL LIVING AREA:
1,222 SQ. FT.

Definitely Detailed

Price Code: C

■ This plan features:

— Three bedrooms

— Two full baths

■ An artistically detailed brick exterior adds to the appeal of this home

■ The Great Room has a wall of windows and a warming fireplace

■ The Kitchen is arranged in a U-shape and features a center island plus a walk-in Pantry

■ An optional plan for the basement includes a Recreation Room, an Exercise Room, and a Bath

■ This home is designed with a basement foundation

MAIN FLOOR — 1,963 SQ. FT.
LOWER FLOOR — 1,963 SQ. FT.

TOTAL LIVING AREA:
1,963 SQ. FT.

To order your Blueprints, call 1-800-235-5700

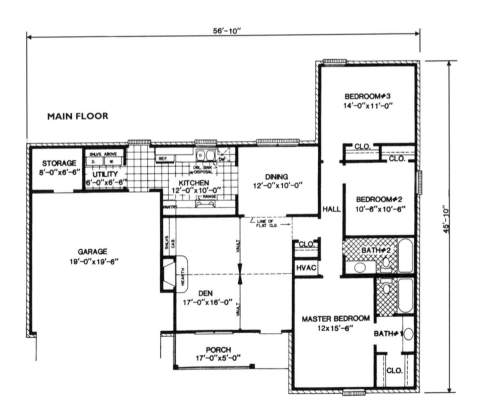

MAIN FLOOR

56'-10"

STORAGE
8'-0"x6'-6"

SHLVS. ABOVE
D.   W.

UTILITY
6'-0"x6'-6"

REF.

DBL SINK
w/DISPOSAL

KITCHEN
12'-0"x10'-0"

RANGE

PANTRY

BEDROOM #3
14'-0"x11'-0"

CLO.

CLO.

DINING
12'-0"x10'-0"

HALL

BEDROOM #2
10'-6"x10'-6"

GARAGE
19'-0"x19'-6"

SHLVS
CAB.

HEARTH

VAULT

VAULT

LINE OF
FLAT CLG.

CLO.

HVAC

BATH #2

DEN
17'-0"x16'-0"

MASTER BEDROOM
12'x15'-6"

BATH #1

PORCH
17'-0"x5'-0"

CLO.

45'-10"

Warm and Inviting

Price Code: A

■ This plan features:

— Three bedrooms

— Two full baths

■ Den with a cozy fireplace and vaulted ceiling

■ Well-equipped Kitchen contains a double sink and built-in Pantry

■ A spacious Master Bedroom with a private Master Bath and walk-in closet

■ Additional Bedrooms share full hall Bath

■ This home is designed with slab and crawlspace foundation options

MAIN FLOOR — 1,363 SQ. FT.
GARAGE — 434 SQ. FT.

TOTAL LIVING AREA:
1,363 SQ. FT.

Striking Style

Price Code: A

- This plan features:
  — Three bedrooms
  — Two full baths

- Windows and exterior detailing create a striking elevation

- The Dining Room has a front window wall and arched openings

- The Great Room has a vaulted ceiling and a fireplace

- The Master Suite features a tray ceiling, a walk-in closet and a private Bath

- This home is designed with basement and crawlspace foundation options

FIRST FLOOR — 1,432 SQ. FT.
BASEMENT — 1,454 SQ. FT.
GARAGE — 440 SQ. FT.

TOTAL LIVING AREA:
1,432 SQ. FT.

MAIN FLOOR

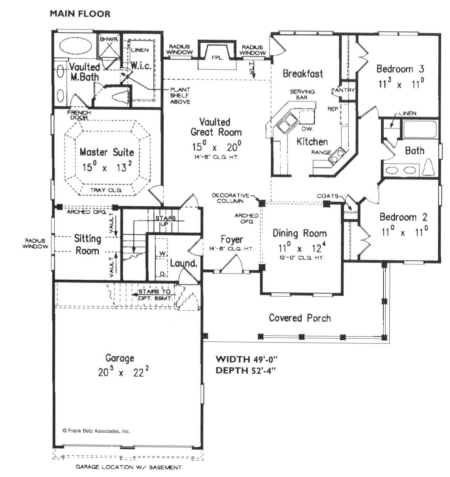

WIDTH 49'-0"
DEPTH 52'-4"

© Frank Betz Associates, Inc.

GARAGE LOCATION W/ BASEMENT

To order your Blueprints, call 1-800-235-5700

Offset Gables add Curb Appeal

Price Code: F

■ This plan features:
— Four bedrooms
— Three full baths
■ A big walk-in closet is conveniently placed off the Master Bath
■ A tall cathedral ceiling rises above the Family Room
■ Drop off the laundry on the way to the Garage
■ Formal and informal Dining Rooms for any occasion
■ A wraparound Patio embellishes the rear elevation
■ This home is designed with a slab foundation

MAIN FLOOR — 2,579 SQ. FT.
GARAGE — 630 SQ. FT.

TOTAL LIVING AREA:
2,579 SQ. FT

MAIN FLOOR

A Big Country Space

Price Code: D

■ This plan features:
— Three bedrooms
— Two full baths
■ This plan is with a two-car Garage set toward the rear is great for corner lots
■ A large Family Room adjoins the Nook and the Kitchen
■ Luxurious appointments in the Master Suite include a large walk-in closet with extra storage space
■ A two-Bedroom Kid's Suite features, Bath, and Study Room
■ This home is designed with a slab foundation

MAIN FLOOR — 2,077 SQ. FT.
GARAGE — 524 SQ. FT.

TOTAL LIVING AREA:
2,077 SQ. FT

WIDTH 70'-8"
DEPTH 69'-0"

MAIN FLOOR

Attention to Detail

Price Code: D

- This plan features:
  — Three bedrooms
  — Three full baths
- From the raised Foyer, a striking view is available through the Great Room and beyond to the covered Deck
- The spacious Kitchen offers an abundance of counter space
- This home is designed with a basement foundation

MAIN FLOOR — 2,041 SQ. FT.
BASEMENT — 1,911 SQ. FT.
GARAGE — 547 SQ. FT.

TOTAL LIVING AREA:
2,041 SQ. FT.

MAIN FLOOR

WIDTH 67'-6"
DEPTH 63'-6"

Ranch with Country Appeal

Price Code: B

- This plan features:
  — Three bedrooms
  — Two full baths
- Tiled Foyer leading into the Living Room
- Sloped ceiling topping the Living Room that is also accented by a fireplace
- Built-in shelves on either side of the arched opening between the Living and Dining Rooms
- Efficient U-shaped Kitchen highlighted by Breakfast Bar
- French door accessing rear Deck from Dining Area
- Master Suite crowned with a decorative ceiling and containing a private whirlpool Bath
- Roomy secondary Bedrooms share a full hall Bath
- This home is designed with basement, slab, and crawlspace foundation options

MAIN FLOOR — 1,539 SQ. FT.
BASEMENT — 1,530 SQ. FT.
GARAGE — 460 SQ. FT.

TOTAL LIVING AREA:
1,539 SQ. FT.

MAIN FLOOR

WIDTH 50'-0"
DEPTH 45'-4"

To order your Blueprints, call 1-800-235-5700

MAIN FLOOR

107' - 4"

68' - 7"

Her Bath

His Bath

Covered Patio

Wet Bar

FamilyRm
16x21
Cathedral Clg

Brkfst
11x14

Bed#3
13x14

MstrBed
15x17
11' Pullman Clg

LivRm
23x17
14' Clg

Kit
14x16

Util

Bed#4
13x12

Pwdr

Gallery

Bed#2
13x14

Study
14x13
14' Clg

Ent
14' Clg

FmlDin
14x14
12' Clg

3-Car Gar
24x34

Covered
Porch

Luxurious Masterpiece

Price Code: K

■ This plan features:

— Four bedrooms

— Three full and one half baths

■ The Expansive formal Living Room has a 14-foot ceiling and a raised hearth fireplace

■ Family Room is highlighted by a fireplace, wetbar, and a cathedral ceiling

■ Hub Kitchen has a cooktop island, peninsula counter/snack bar, and a bright Breakfast Area

■ French doors lead into the Study

■ Private Master Bedroom is enhanced by a pullman ceiling and lavish his and her Baths

■ This home is designed with basement and slab foundation options

MAIN FLOOR — 3,818 SQ. FT.
GARAGE — 816 SQ. FT.

TOTAL LIVING AREA:
3,818 SQ. FT.

153

Inviting Porch

Price Code: A

■ This plan features:

— Three bedrooms

— Two full baths

■ A large and spacious Living Room adjoins the Dining Room for ease in entertaining

■ A private Bedroom wing provides a quiet atmosphere

■ The Master Bedroom has his and her closets and a private Bath

■ The efficient Kitchen features a walk-in Pantry

■ This home is designed with basement and slab foundation options

MAIN FLOOR — 1,243 SQ. FT.
BASEMENT — 1,103 SQ. FT.
GARAGE — 490 SQ. FT.

TOTAL LIVING AREA:
1,243 SQ. FT.

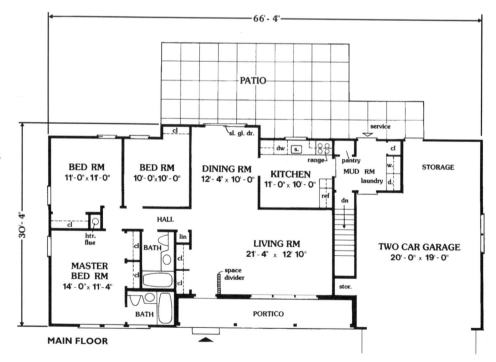

To order your Blueprints, call 1-800-235-5700

MAIN FLOOR

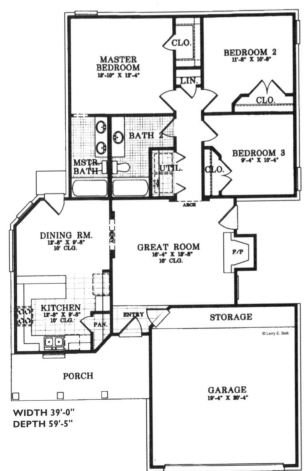

CLO.

MASTER BEDROOM
15'-10" X 13'-4"

BEDROOM 2
11'-8" X 10'-4"

LIN.

CLO.

BATH 2

BEDROOM 3
9'-4" X 10'-4"

MSTR. BATH

UTIL.

CLO.

ARCH

DINING RM.
12'-8" X 9'-8"
10' CLG.

GREAT ROOM
16'-4" X 18'-8"
10' CLG.

F/P

KITCHEN
12'-8" X 9'-8"
10' CLG.

PAN.

ENTRY

STORAGE

© Larry E. Belk

PORCH

GARAGE
19'-4" X 20'-4"

WIDTH 39'-0"
DEPTH 59'-5"

Bedroom Cul-de-sac

Price Code: A

■ This plan features:

— Three bedrooms

— Two full baths

■ The simplicity of the facade, with its discreet details, gives this home welcoming appeal

■ A volume ceiling, focal point fireplace, and arched Entries give the Great Room grace and character

■ Counter space and tile define the efficient Kitchen that overlooks a window-lined Dining Area

■ The Bedrooms share the privacy of the rear wing

■ This home is designed with a slab foundation

MAIN FLOOR — 1,249 SQ. FT.
GARAGE — 444 SQ. FT.
PORCH — 125 SQ. FT.

TOTAL LIVING AREA:
1,249 SQ. FT.

Quoins add Interest

Price Code: B

■ This plan features:

— Three bedrooms

— Two full baths

■ Stucco, quoins, and keystones give this home great curb appeal

■ Columns enhance the Foyer and entrance to the Dining Room

■ The galley-style Kitchen has easy access to the Breakfast Area, the Dining Room, and the Utility Room

■ The Master Bedroom Suite features a corner walk-in closet that adjoins the double-vanity Master Bath

■ This home is designed with crawlspace and slab foundation options

MAIN FLOOR — 1,704 SQ. FT.

TOTAL LIVING AREA:
1,704 SQ. FT.

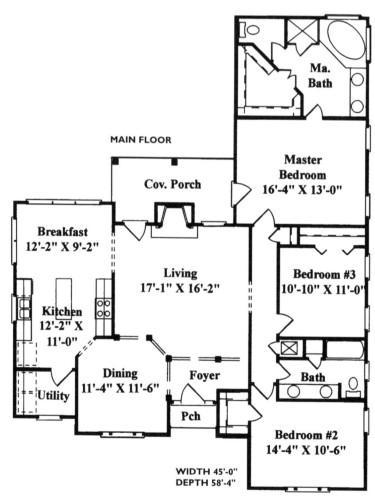

MAIN FLOOR

Ma. Bath

Master Bedroom
16'-4" X 13'-0"

Cov. Porch

Breakfast
12'-2" X 9'-2"

Living
17'-1" X 16'-2"

Bedroom #3
10'-10" X 11'-0"

Kitchen
12'-2" X 11'-0"

Dining
11'-4" X 11'-6"

Foyer

Bath

Utility

Pch

Bedroom #2
14'-4" X 10'-6"

WIDTH 45'-0"
DEPTH 58'-4"

To order your Blueprints, call 1-800-235-5700

Taseful and Polished

Price Code: E

- This plan features:
  - Four bedrooms
  - Two full baths
- A columned front Porch provides guests with a grand entrance
- The L-shaped Kitchen is conveniently placed for easy access to the Dining Room, Breakfast Area, and Living Room
- Bedrooms flank the Living Areas in this split-Bedroom design
- The Master Bedroom features a luxurious Master Bath and walk-in closets
- This home is designed with crawlspace and slab foundation options

MAIN FLOOR — 2,365 SQ. FT.

TOTAL LIVING AREA:
2,365 SQ. FT.

WIDTH 67'-6"
DEPTH 73'-0"

MAIN FLOOR

Angled Front Porch

Price Code: E

- This plan features:
  - Four bedrooms
  - Three full baths
- The Master Bedroom opens onto a covered back Porch
- A Computer Room can double as a home office
- This home is designed with a slab foundation

MAIN FLOOR — 2,450 SQ. FT.
GARAGE — 427 SQ. FT.

TOTAL LIVING AREA:
2,450 SQ. FT.

MAIN FLOOR

WIDTH 66'-10'
DEPTH 64'-11"

Arches add Curb Appeal

Price Code: E

- This plan features:
— Four bedrooms
— Three full baths

- The Master Bath includes a large soaking tub

- The open design of the common areas promotes family activity

- All Bedrooms are isolated in the right wing for privacy

- This home is designed with a slab foundation

MAIN FLOOR — 2,471 SQ. FT.
GARAGE — 566 SQ. FT.

TOTAL LIVING AREA:
2,471 SQ. FT.

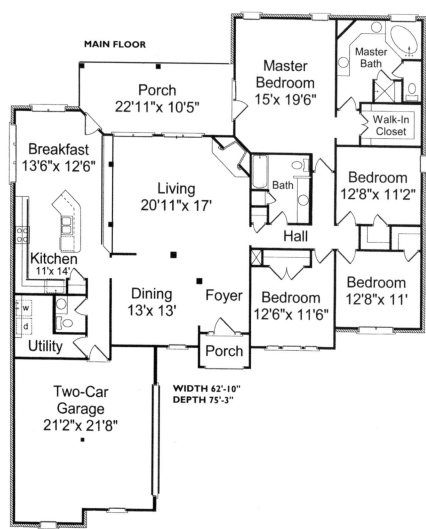

MAIN FLOOR

Porch 22'11"x 10'5"

Master Bedroom 15'x 19'6"

Master Bath

Walk-In Closet

Breakfast 13'6"x 12'6"

Living 20'11"x 17'

Bath

Bedroom 12'8"x 11'2"

Kitchen 11'x 14'

Hall

Dining 13'x 13'

Foyer

Bedroom 12'6"x 11'6"

Bedroom 12'8"x 11'

w d

Utility

Porch

Two-Car Garage 21'2"x 21'8"

WIDTH 62'-10"
DEPTH 75'-3"

High Ceilings and Open Spaces

Price Code: E

■ This plan features:
  — Three bedrooms
  — Three full baths
■ A tiled Foyer leads into the Dining Area that flows uninhibited into the Great Room
■ The Kitchen has a snack bar, built-in Pantry, and Breakfast Area, and is adjacent to the Keeping Room with a fireplace
■ This home is designed with a crawlspace foundation

MAIN FLOOR — 2,330 SQ. FT.
BASEMENT — 2,330 SQ. FT.
GARAGE — 416 SQ. FT.

TOTAL LIVING AREA:
2,330 SQ. FT.

Built Around a Truly Great Room

Price Code: H

■ This plan features:
  — Four bedrooms
  — Three full baths
  — Two full, one half, and one three-quarter baths
■ The Elegant Study is enhanced by a private fireplace
■ Master Bedroom opens to the Gallery and onto a Covered Patio
■ This home is designed with a slab foundation

MAIN FLOOR — 3,162 SQ. FT.
GARAGE — 662 SQ. FT.

TOTAL LIVING AREA:
3,162 SQ. FT.

To order your Blueprints, call 1-800-235-5700

PLAN NO. 94672

Possible Home Office

Price Code: E

■ This plan features:

— Four bedrooms

— Three full baths

■ French doors look out onto the back Porch

■ Carry the groceries directly from the car to the Kitchen

■ This home is designed with a slab foundation

MAIN FLOOR — 2,391 SQ. FT.

GARAGE — 595 SQ. FT

TOTAL LIVING AREA:

2,391 SQ. FT.

MAIN FLOOR

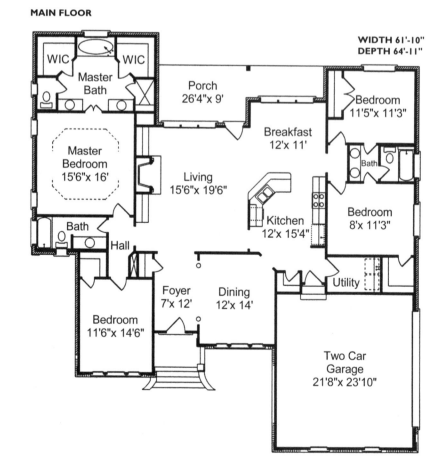

WIDTH 61'-10"
DEPTH 64'-11"

← 40'-0" →

MAIN FLOOR

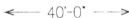

Covered Patio

MstrBed
15x13
11'0" Vaulted Clg.
From 8'-0"

9'-0" Clg.

Walk-In Closet

Din
9x13
10'-0" Clg.

Kit
11x13
Pantry

Bed#2
11x10

Linen

9'-0" Clg.

Bed#3
10x12

Util

LivRm
14x22
10'-0" Clg.

Coats
10' Clg.

Ent

Por

Gar
20x22

60'-8"

Brick Abounds

Price Code: B

■ This plan features:

— Three bedrooms

— Two full baths

■ The covered front Porch opens into the Entry that has a 10-foot ceiling and a coat closet

■ The Dining Room features a 10-foot ceiling and access to the Patio

■ The Kitchen is angled and has a Pantry and a cooktop island

■ The Master Bedroom is located in the rear for privacy and boasts a triangular walk-in closet

■ This home is designed with a slab foundation

MAIN FLOOR — 1,528 SQ. FT.
GARAGE — 440 SQ. FT.

TOTAL LIVING AREA:
1,528 SQ. FT.

Traditional Simplicity

Price Code: D

■ This plan features:

— Three bedrooms

— Two full baths

■ The Living Room features a decorative ceiling, focal point fireplace, and access to the rear Porch

■ Columns delineate the Dining Room from the Foyer and Living Room

■ The Master Bath features a twin vanity, separate shower and tub, and two walk-in closets

■ This home is designed with a slab foundation

MAIN FLOOR — 2,232 SQ. FT.

TOTAL LIVING AREA:
2,232 SQ. FT.

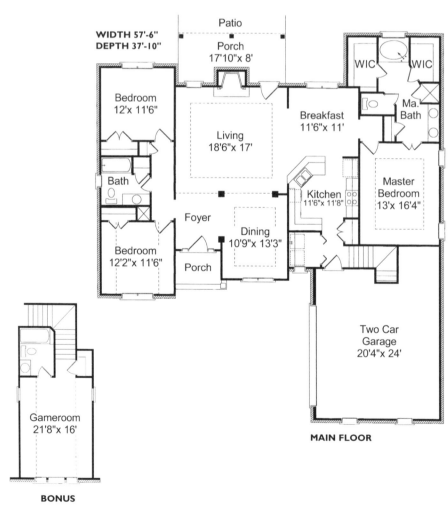

WIDTH 57'-6"
DEPTH 37'-10"

Patio

Porch
17'10"x 8'

WIC   WIC

Bedroom
12'x 11'6"

Living
18'6"x 17'

Breakfast
11'6"x 11'

Ma.
Bath

Bath

Kitchen
11'6"x 11'8"

Master
Bedroom
13'x 16'4"

Foyer

Dining
10'9"x 13'3"

Bedroom
12'2"x 11'6"

Porch

Two Car
Garage
20'4"x 24'

MAIN FLOOR

Gameroom
21'8"x 16'

BONUS

To order your Blueprints, call 1-800-235-5700

Master Bedroom 14'4"x 18'4"

Covered Porch 21'5"x 10'6"

WIDTH 64'-10"
DEPTH 76'-9"

Walk-In Closet

Walk-In Closet

Living 21'6"x 23'

Breakfast 14'x 11'4"

Bedroom 12'6"x 11'6"

Master Bath

Kitchen 14'x 13'

Bath

Dressing

Bath

Foyer

Utility

Bedroom 12'x 12'

Bedroom 11'10"x 13'

Porch

Dining 14'5"x 14'

Two Car Garage 21'2"x 26'

MAIN FLOOR

Unfinished Gameroom 11'4"x 26'

BONUS

Past and Present Converge

Price Code: F

■ This plan features:

— Four bedrooms

— Three full baths

■ The Living Room features a focal point fireplace, built-ins, and a wall of windows

■ Two columns adorn the entrance to the formal Dining Room

■ The Kitchen is designed for efficiency and convenience

■ The secluded Master Bedroom features a decorative ceiling

■ A fourth Bedroom next to the Master Suite could be used as a Nursery

■ This home is designed with a slab foundation

MAIN FLOOR — 2,781 SQ. FT.
BONUS — 319 SQ. FT.
GARAGE — 623 SQ. FT.

TOTAL LIVING AREA:
2,781 SQ. FT.

One Floor Convenience

Price Code: F

- This plan features:
— Four bedrooms
— Three full baths

- A distinguished brick exterior adds curb appeal

- A Formal Entry/Gallery opens to the large Living Room with a hearth fireplace

- The Efficient Kitchen, with angled counters and serving bar, easily serves the Breakfast Room, Patio, and formal Dining Room

- The Corner Master Bedroom is enhanced by a vaulted ceiling and pampering Bath with a large walk-in closet

- This home is designed with a slab foundation

MAIN FLOOR — 2,675 SQ. FT.
GARAGE — 638 SQ. FT.

TOTAL LIVING AREA:
2,675 SQ. FT.

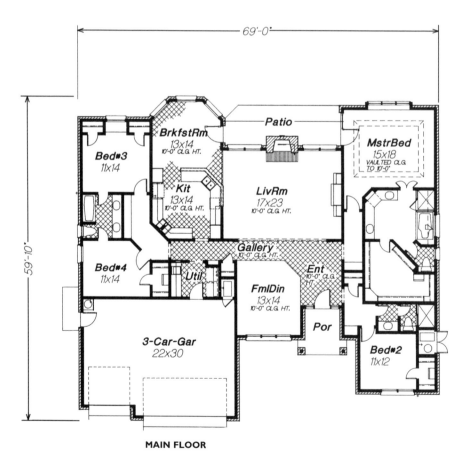

MAIN FLOOR

To order your Blueprints, call 1-800-235-5700

Open Air Ranch

Price Code: C

- This plan features:
  - Four bedrooms
  - Two full baths
- The Dining Room features doors to the rear Patio
- A convenient U-shaped Kitchen is highlighted by a double sink, a Pantry, and ample counter space
- A Laundry/Utility Room is located off of the two-car Garage
- Three Bedrooms share a full Bath
- The Master Bedroom has two closets and a private Bath with dual vanities
- This home is designed with basement, slab, and crawlspace foundation options

MAIN FLOOR — 1,901 SQ. FT.
GARAGE — 420 SQ. FT.

TOTAL LIVING AREA:
1,901 SQ. FT.

MAIN FLOOR

Patio

MBr 1
12 x 16-8

Br 2
10-4 x 10-10

Family Rm
14-8 x 13-2

Dining
10-8 x 13-2

Kit
10-6 x 13-2

W D L

optional Fireplace

Living
15-8 x 17-6

DN
pan.

Garage
20-6 x 20-6

Br 3
10 x 11-2

Br 4
10 x 11-2

Foy

34'0"

68'0"

OPTIONAL CRAWLSPACE/SLAB

Especially Surprising

Price Code: A

- This plan features:
  - Three bedrooms
  - Two full baths
- Graceful columns support the covered Entry
- The tiled Foyer leads directly into the Great Room that has a rear wall fireplace and a cathedral ceiling
- The Kitchen has an arched pass-through to the Great Room and is open to the Dining Room with a cathedral ceiling
- The Screen Porch is accessed from the Dining Room
- The Master Suite has a plant ledge, fireplace, tray ceiling, walk-in closet, and a fully-appointed Bath
- Two other Bedrooms have access to a full Bath in the hall
- This home is designed with a basement foundation

MAIN FLOOR — 1,495 SQ. FT.
BASEMENT — 1,495 SQ. FT.

TOTAL LIVING AREA:
1,495 SQ. FT.

SCREEN PORCH
12'8" x 12'

DIN.
CATHEDRAL CEILING
12'9" x 12'

BR.#3
10'8" x 10'4"

GRT. RM.
CATHEDRAL CEILING
12'8" x 19'9"

KIT.
10' x 10'6"

MBR
TRAY CEILING
13'3" x 15'3"

PLANT LEDGE

BR.#2
CATHEDRAL CEILING
10'9" x 10'4"

2 CAR GAR.
20' x 20'

58'8"

48'0"

MAIN FLOOR

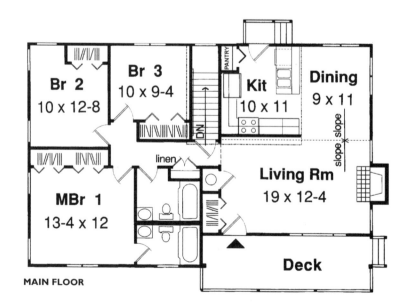

PLAN NO. 34003

Delightful and Compact

Price Code: A

■ This plan features:

— Three bedrooms

— Two full baths

■ A Living Room, with fireplace, further enhanced by a wonderful picture window

■ A counter island featuring double sinks separating the Kitchen and Dining Areas

■ A Master Bedroom that includes a private Master Bath and double closets

■ Two additional Bedrooms with ample closet space that share a full Bath

■ This home is designed with basement, slab, and crawlpace foundation options

MAIN FLOOR — 1,146 SQ. FT.

TOTAL LIVING AREA:
1,146 SQ. FT.

OPTIONAL
CRAWLSPACE/SLAB

Rear Elevation

Br 2
10 x 12-8

Br 3
10 x 9-4

Kit
10 x 11

Dining
9 x 11

linen

MBr 1
13-4 x 12

Living Rm
19 x 12-4

PANTRY

Deck

MAIN FLOOR

166

To order your Blueprints, call 1-800-235-5700

MAIN FLOOR

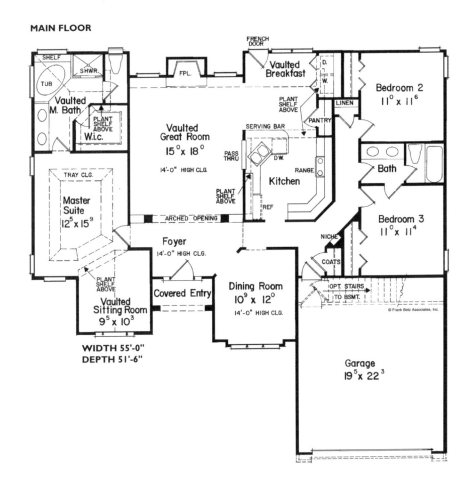

WIDTH 55'-0"
DEPTH 51'-6"

High Ceilings add Volume

Price Code: B

■ This plan features:

— Three bedrooms

— Two full baths

■ A covered Entry gives way to a 14-foot high ceiling in the Foyer

■ An arched opening greets you in the Great Room

■ The Master Suite has a tray ceiling, a vaulted Stitting Area, and a private Bath

■ This home is designed with basement, slab, and crawlspace foundation options

MAIN FLOOR — 1,715 SQ. FT.
BASEMENT — 1,715 SQ. FT.
GARAGE — 450 SQ. FT.

TOTAL LIVING AREA:
1,715 SQ. FT.

Arches are Appealing

Price Code: B

- This plan features:
  — Three bedrooms
  — Two full baths

- The welcoming front Porch is enhanced by graceful columns and curved windows

- The expansive Great Room is accented by a corner fireplace

- Open and convenient, the Kitchen includes a work island, angled peninsula counter/eating bar, and nearby Laundry and Garage Entry

- The secluded Master Bedroom boasts a luxurious Bath

- This home is designed with basement, slab, and crawlspace foundation options

MAIN FLOOR — 1,642 SQ. FT.
BASEMENT — 1,642 SQ. FT.
GARAGE — 430 SQ. FT.

TOTAL LIVING AREA:
1,642 SQ. FT.

**OPTIONAL BASEMENT
STAIR LOCATION**

WIDTH 59'-0"
DEPTH 44'-0"

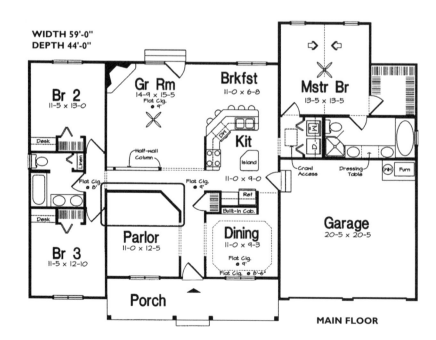

MAIN FLOOR

To order your Blueprints, call 1-800-235-5700

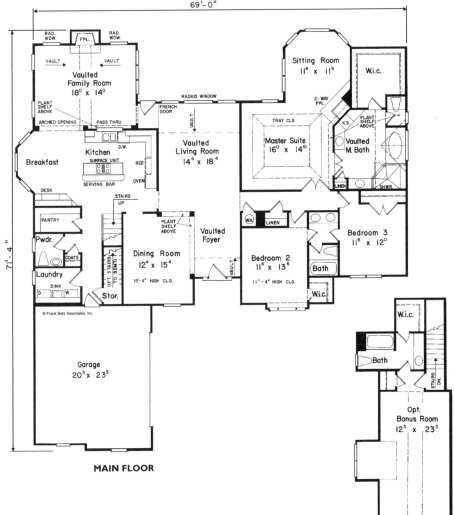

MAIN FLOOR

BONUS

Delightful Detailing

Price Code: F

■ This plan features:

— Three bedrooms

— Two full and one half baths

■ The vaulted ceiling extends from the Foyer into the Living Room

■ The family Room has a vaulted ceiling and a fireplace

■ The Master Suite is highlighted by a Sitting Room, walk-in closet, and private Bath with a vaulted ceiling

■ This home is designed with basement and crawlspace foundation options

MAIN FLOOR — 2,622 SQ. FT.
BONUS ROOM — 478 SQ. FT.
BASEMENT — 2,622 SQ. FT.
GARAGE — 506 SQ. FT.

TOTAL LIVING AREA:
2,622 SQ. FT.

Relaxing Lanai

Price Code: F

■ This plan features:

— Three bedrooms

— Two full and one half baths

■ The Foyer provides a view through the interior to the Covered Lanai, which is accessed from the Grand Room, Breakfast Room, and Master Suite

■ The Kitchen accommodates the angled Gathering Room and Breakfast Nook

■ This home is designed with basement and crawlspace foundation options

MAIN FLOOR — 2,585 SQ. FT.
BONUS ROOM — 519 SQ. FT.
BASEMENT — 2,609 SQ. FT.
GARAGE — 607 SQ. FT.

TOTAL LIVING AREA:
2,585 SQ. FT.

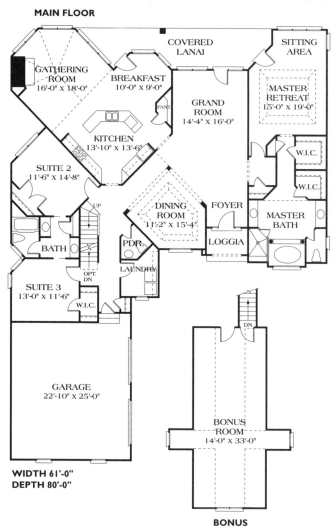

MAIN FLOOR

COVERED LANAI

SITTING AREA

GATHERING ROOM 16'-0" x 18'-0"

BREAKFAST 10'-0" x 9'-0"

GRAND ROOM 14'-4" x 16'-0"

MASTER RETREAT 15'-0" x 19'-0"

PANT.

KITCHEN 13'-10" x 13'-6"

W.I.C.

W.I.C.

SUITE 2 11'-6" x 14'-8"

UP

DINING ROOM 11'-2" x 15'-4"

FOYER

MASTER BATH

BATH

PDR.

LOGGIA

OPT. DN

LAUNDRY

SUITE 3 13'-0" x 11'-6"

W.I.C.

DN

GARAGE 22'-10" x 25'-0"

BONUS ROOM 14'-0" x 33'-0"

WIDTH 61'-0"
DEPTH 80'-0"

BONUS

Double Arches add Elegance

Price Code: C

■ This plan features:
— Three bedrooms
— Two full baths
■ Double arches form the Entrance to this elegantly styled home
■ Two palladian windows add distinction to the elevation and give the home a timeless appeal
■ The Kitchen features an angled eating bar and opens to both the Breakfast Room and Living Room
■ The Master Suite includes a Master Bath with all the amenities, including a huge walk-in closet
■ This home is designed with a crawlspace and slab foundation

MAIN FLOOR — 1,932 SQ. FT.
GARAGE — 552 SQ. FT.

TOTAL LIVING AREA:
1,932 SQ. FT.

COPYRIGHT LARRY E. BELK

WIDTH 65'-10"
DEPTH 53'-5"

Southampton-Style Cottage

Price Code: F

■ This plan features:
— Three bedrooms
— Two full baths
■ Stairs lead up to the covered Entry Porch and into the Foyer
■ An arched opening leads into the Grand Room, which has a fireplace
■ Five French doors in various rooms open out onto the rear Lanai
■ The Kitchen has a walk-in Pantry located next to the Nook
■ On the opposite side of the home are a Study and the Master Suite
■ The space on the ground level can be finished into a Recreation Room
■ This home is designed with pier/post foundation options
■ Alternate foundation options available at an additional charge. Please call 1-800-235-5700 for more information.

MAIN FLOOR — 2,068 SQ. FT.
LOWER FLOOR — 1,402 SQ. FT.
GARAGE — 560 SQ. FT.

TOTAL LIVING AREA:
2,068 SQ. FT.

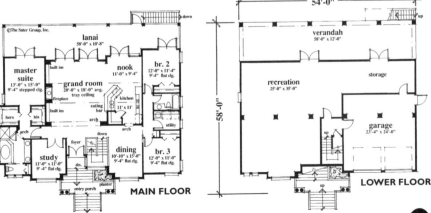

171

To order your Blueprints, call 1-800-235-5700

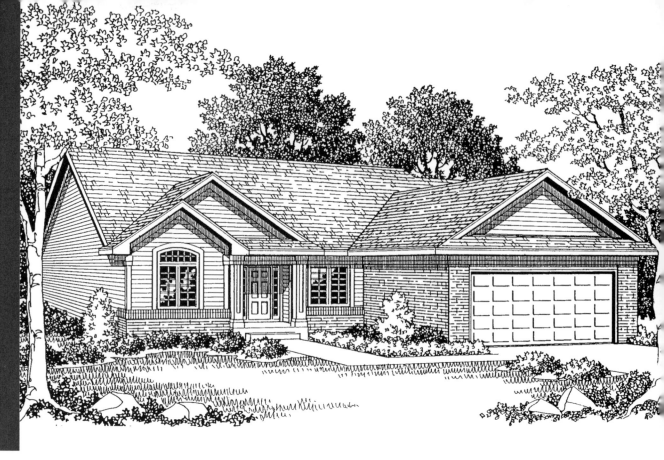

PLAN NO. 97113

Direct-Vent Fireplace

Price Code: A

■ This plan features:

— Three bedrooms

— Two full baths

■ A vaulted ceiling adds grand scale to the Entry

■ A cathedral ceiling and wall of windows in the Dining Area create a pleasant dining atmosphere

■ The Master Suite features a tiled, full Bath and a walk-in closet

■ Secondary Bedrooms, one featuring a cathedral ceiling, share a hall and a tiled, full Bath in the left wing of the home

■ This home is designed with a basement foundation

MAIN FLOOR — 1,416 SQ. FT.
BASEMENT — 1,416 SQ. FT.

TOTAL LIVING AREA:
1,416 SQ. FT.

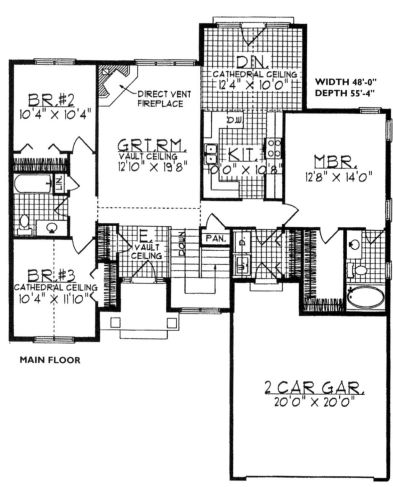

WIDTH 48'-0"
DEPTH 55'-4"

DIRECT VENT FIREPLACE

BR. #2
10'4" X 10'4"

D.N.
CATHEDRAL CEILING
12'4" X 10'0"

GRT. RM.
VAULT CEILING
12'10" X 19'8"

KIT.
10'0" X 10'8"

MBR.
12'8" X 14'0"

E.
VAULT CEILING

DOWN

PAN.

BR. #3
CATHEDRAL CEILING
10'4" X 11'10"

MAIN FLOOR

2 CAR GAR.
20'0" X 20'0"

172

To order your Blueprints, call 1-800-235-5700

All About Detail

Price Code: A

■ This plan features:

— Three bedrooms

— Two full baths

■ The Foyer, with 12'-10" ceiling, leads directly into the Great Room, instantly welcoming family and friends

■ The impressive Master Suite features a tray ceiling, window-lined Sitting Room, and a French door leading to the vaulted Master Bath and spacious walk-in closet

■ Light pours in through the Breakfast Area's windows

■ A serving bar makes dining possible in both the Kitchen and the Great Room

■ This home is designed with basement and crawlspace foundation options

MAIN FLOOR — 1,354 SQ. FT.
BASEMENT — 1,390 SQ. FT.
GARAGE — 434 SQ. FT.

TOTAL LIVING AREA:
1,354 SQ. FT.

For The Busy Family

Price Code: D

■ This plan features:

— Four Bedrooms

— Three full baths

■ From the Entry, traffic flows to the Gallery, Formal Dining Area, and Living Room with a cozy fireplace situated between bookshelves

■ Open and efficient, the Kitchen easily serves the Breakfast Alcove, the Patio, and Dining Area

■ Two Bedrooms, one with two closets and a window seat, share a full Bath, while, the fourth Bedroom has a separate Bath

■ This home is designed with a slab foundation

MAIN FLOOR — 2,233 SQ. FT.
GARAGE — 635 SQ. FT.

TOTAL LIVING AREA:
2,233 SQ. FT.

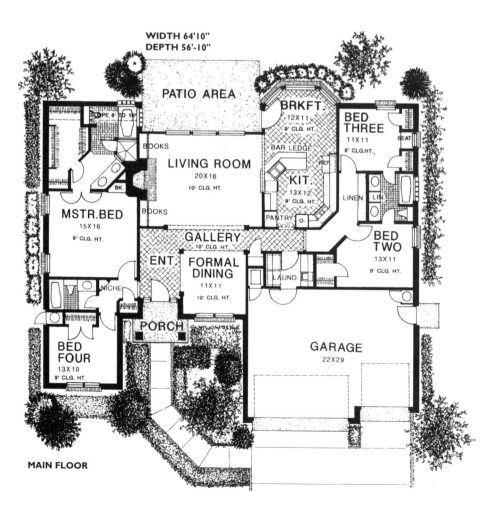

WIDTH 64'10"
DEPTH 56'-10"

MAIN FLOOR

174   To order your Blueprints, call 1-800-235-5700

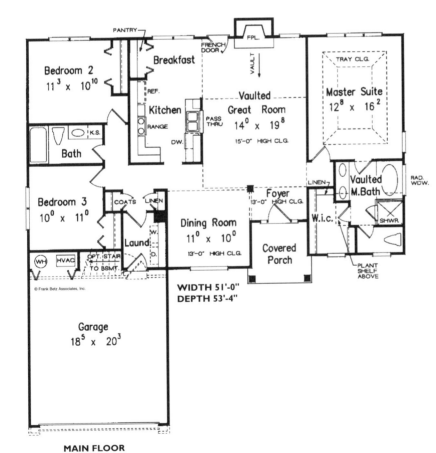

MAIN FLOOR

Elegant Arched Entrance
Price Code: A

■ This plan features:

— Three bedrooms

— Two full baths

■ The Covered Porch leads to an open Foyer, which gives way to a vaulted Great Room

■ Elegant arches and peaks decorate the exterior of this home

■ The Master Suite is accented with a tray ceiling and a private Bath

■ This home is designed with basement and crawlspace foundation options

MAIN FLOOR — 1,459 SQ. FT.
BASEMENT — 1,466 SQ. FT.
GARAGE — 390 SQ. FT.

TOTAL LIVING AREA:
1,459 SQ. FT.

Spacious Living Room

Price Code: E

■ This plan features:
— Four bedrooms
— Three full and one half baths
■ The spacious Living Room is topped by a decorative ceiling and is enhanced by a corner fireplace
■ The Kitchen boasts a built-in desk and an angled counter/snack bar
■ The secluded Master Suite has two walk-in closets and a five-piece Bath
■ This home is designed with basement and crawlspace foundation options

MAIN FLOOR — 2,483 SQ. FT.
GARAGE — 504 SQ. FT.

TOTAL LIVING AREA:
2,483 SQ. FT.

MAIN FLOOR

Cabin in the Country

Price Code: A

■ This plan features:
— Two bedrooms
— One full and one half baths
■ The Screened Porch offers three seasons of outdoor enjoyment
■ The combination Living and Dining Area has a cozy fireplace for added warmth
■ The efficiently laid out Kitchen features a built-in Pantry
■ Two large Bedrooms are located at the rear of the home
■ This home is designed with slab and crawlspace foundation options

MAIN FLOOR — 928 SQ. FT.
PORCH — 230 SQ. FT.

TOTAL LIVING AREA:
928 SQ. FT.

MAIN FLOOR

To order your Blueprints, call 1-800-235-5700

Outstanding Family Home

Price Code: D

■ This plan features:

— Three bedrooms

— Two full baths

■ The split-Bedroom layout is the perfect floor plan for a family with older children

■ The Great Room features a cozy fireplace, access to the rear Porch, and an open layout into the Nook and Kitchen

■ The Master Suite has access to the rear Porch, a pampering Bath and a walk-in closet

■ This home is designed with slab and crawlspace foundation options

MAIN FLOOR — 2,162 SQ. FT.
GARAGE — 498 SQ. FT.

TOTAL LIVING AREA:
2,162 SQ. FT.

70'

50'

PORCH

MASTER SUITE
14 × 19
10'-0" CEILING

BATH

SHWR

LIN

CLOSET

SHELVES

NOOK
11 × 10

PANTRY

OVEN

RNG

BAR

KITCHEN
13 × 14

D.W.

REFG

STO

P/P

GREAT RM
18 × 24
10'-0" CEILING

FAN

FAN

BEDRM
11 × 12

STO

CLO

BATH

STO

CLO

CLO

BEDRM
12 × 12

GARAGE
21 × 23

FRZR

UTIL.
7 × 10

WASH

DRY

DINING
10 × 12
10'-0" CEIL.

FOYER
10' CEIL.

A/C

STUDY
9 × 10

CLO

PORCH

MAIN FLOOR

Skylight Brightens Master Bedroom

Price Code: B

■ This plan features:

— Three bedrooms

— Two full baths

■ A covered Porch Entry

■ The Living Room is enhanced by a vaulted beam ceiling and a fireplace

■ The Master Bedroom has a decorative ceiling and a skylight in the private Bath

■ The optional Deck is accessible through sliding doors off the Master Bedroom

■ This home is designed with basement, slab, and crawlspace foundation options

MAIN FLOOR — 1,686 SQ. FT.
BASEMENT — 1,676 SQ. FT.
GARAGE — 484 SQ. FT.

TOTAL LIVING AREA:
1,686 SQ. FT.

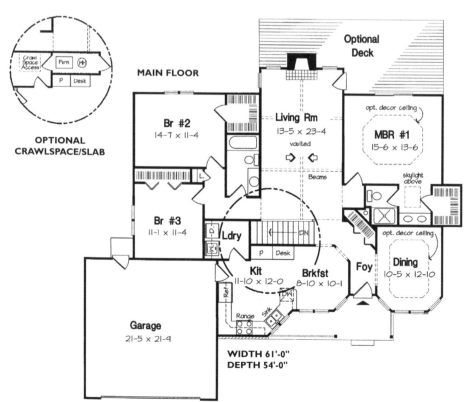

Rear Elevation

OPTIONAL CRAWLSPACE/SLAB

MAIN FLOOR

Br #2
14-7 x 11-4

Br #3
11-1 x 11-4

Ldry

Kit
11-10 x 12-0

Brkfst
8-10 x 10-1

Garage
21-5 x 21-9

Living Rm
13-5 x 23-4
vaulted

Beams

Optional Deck

opt. decor ceiling

MBR #1
15-6 x 13-6

skylight above

opt. decor ceiling

Foy

Dining
10-5 x 12-10

WIDTH 61'-0"
DEPTH 54'-0"

To order your Blueprints, call 1-800-235-5700

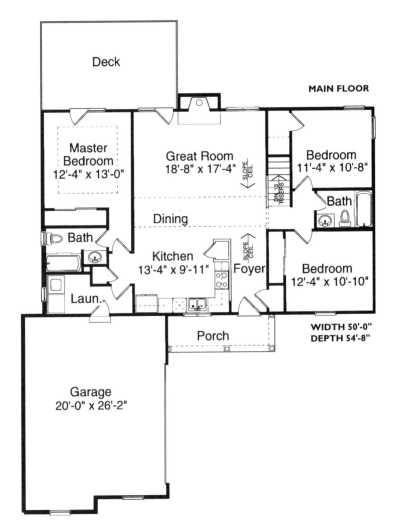

Deck

MAIN FLOOR

Master Bedroom
12'-4" x 13'-0"

Great Room
18'-8" x 17'-4"

SLOPE CEIL.

Bedroom
11'-4" x 10'-8"

DN 13 RISERS

Bath

Dining

Bath

SLOPE CEIL.

Kitchen
13'-4" x 9'-11"

Foyer

Bedroom
12'-4" x 10'-10"

Laun.

Porch

WIDTH 50'-0"
DEPTH 54'-8"

Garage
20'-0" x 26'-2"

Stone Accents

Price Code: A

■ This plan features:

— Three bedrooms

— Two full baths

■ A sloped ceiling unites the open Kitchen, Dining Area, Great Room, and Foyer

■ The Master Bedroom features a tray ceiling and access to the Deck

■ The position of the Garage door allows this design to fit a narrower lot

■ This home is designed with a basement foundation

MAIN FLOOR — 1,315 SQ. FT.
BASEMENT — 1,315 SQ. FT.
GARAGE — 488 SQ. FT.

TOTAL LIVING AREA:
1,315 SQ. FT.

Attractive Exterior

Price Code: D

■ This plan features:

— Three bedrooms

— Two full baths

■ In the gallery columns separate space into the Great Room and the Dining Room

■ The large Kitchen is a chef's dream with lots of counter space and a Pantry

■ The Master Bedroom is removed from traffic areas and contains a luxurious Master Bath

■ This home is designed with a slab foundation

MAIN FLOOR — 2,167 SQ. FT.
GARAGE — 690 SQ. FT.

TOTAL LIVING AREA:
2,167 SQ. FT.

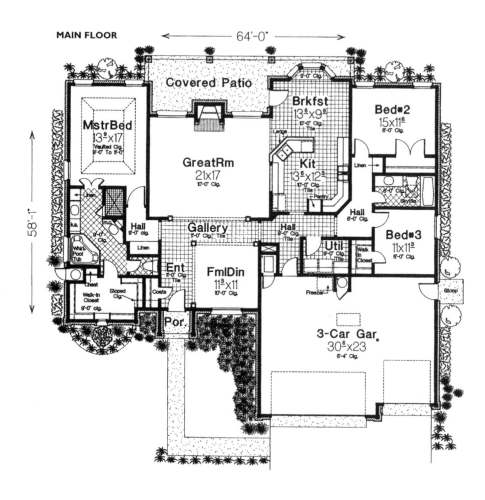

MAIN FLOOR

To order your Blueprints, call 1-800-235-5700

Central Great Room
Anchors the Home

Price Code: A

■ This plan features:
— Three bedrooms
— Two full baths

■ The Kitchen, Dining Room, and Great Room
share a large open space

■ A graceful arch leads to the front Entry

■ The Master Bath features separate tub
and shower

■ Plans include a Deck or Patio off the
Great Room

■ A large walk-in closet completes
the Master Suite

■ This home is designed with basement, slab, and
crawlspace foundation options

MAIN FLOOR — 1,383 SQ. FT.
BASEMENT — 1,460 SQ. FT.
GARAGE — 416 SQ. FT.

TOTAL LIVING AREA:
1,383 SQ. FT

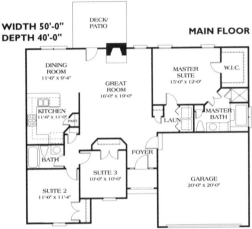

WIDTH 50'-0"
DEPTH 40'-0"

MAIN FLOOR

European Styling

Price Code: E

■ This plan features:
— Three bedrooms
— Two full and one half baths

■ The Kitchen features an island bar, double sink
and a Pantry

■ The home has two fireplaces, one in the Great
Room the other in the Gathering Room

■ The Master Suite features dual walk-in closets
and a five-piece Bath

■ This home is designed with a basement and
crawlspace foundation options

MAIN FLOOR — 2,290 SQ. FT.
BASEMENT — 2,290 SQ. FT.
BONUS — 304 SQ. FT.
GARAGE — 544 SQ. FT.

TOTAL LIVING AREA:
2,290 SQ. FT.

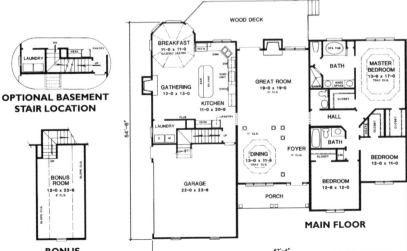

OPTIONAL BASEMENT
STAIR LOCATION

BONUS

MAIN FLOOR

European Styling

Price Code: C

- This plan features:
— Three bedrooms
— Two full and one half baths
- French doors in the Study open to a long view to the Kitchen
- The Great Room leads to the covered Patio
- The Master Bedroom has a sloped 10-foot-high ceiling; all other rooms have 9 or 10-foot-high ceilings
- This home is designed with a slab foundation

MAIN FLOOR — 1,902 SQ. FT.
GARAGE — 636 SQ. FT.

TOTAL LIVING AREA:
1,902 SQ. FT.

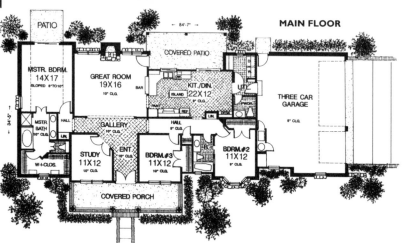

MAIN FLOOR

Lavishly Appointed

Price Code: E

- This plan features:
— Three bedrooms
— Two full and one half bath
- The stone and stucco exterior with stucco details creates a great first impression
- A 14-foot coffered ceiling graces the sumptuous Family Room
- Upstairs, an optional Bedroom and Bath would be great for a future teenager
- The fabulous Master Suite features a vaulted ceiling and his and hers walk-in closets
- This home is designed with basement and crawlspace foundation options

MAIN FLOOR — 2,403 SQ. FT
GARAGE — 488 SQ. FT.
BASEMENT — 2,403 SQ. FT.
BONUS ROOM — 285 SQ. FT.

TOTAL LIVING AREA:
2,403 SQ. FT.

WIDTH 60'-0"
DEPTH 67'-0"

MAIN FLOOR

BONUS

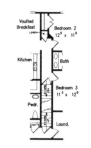

**OPTIONAL BASEMENT
STAIR LOCATION**

To order your Blueprints, call 1-800-235-5700

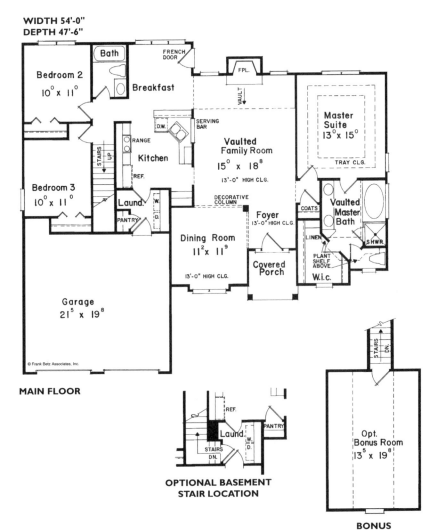

WIDTH 54'-0"
DEPTH 47'-6"

MAIN FLOOR

© Frank Betz Associates, Inc.

OPTIONAL BASEMENT
STAIR LOCATION

BONUS

European Flair

Price Code: B

■ This plan features:

— Three bedrooms

— Two full baths

■ Fireplace serves as an attractive focal point for the vaulted Family Room

■ Master Suite topped by a tray ceiling over the Bedroom and a vaulted ceiling over the Master Bath

■ This home is designed with basement and crawlspace foundation options

MAIN FLOOR — 1,544 SQ. FT.
BONUS ROOM — 284 SQ. FT.
BASEMENT — 1,544 SQ. FT.
GARAGE — 440 SQ. FT.

TOTAL LIVING AREA:
1,544 SQ. FT.

Luxurious Living

Price Code: I

■ This plan features:

— Four bedrooms

— Two full and one three-quarter baths

■ Decorative windows enhance front entrance of elegant home

■ Formal Living Room accented by fireplace

■ Breakfast Bar, work island, and an abundance of storage and counter space featured in Kitchen

■ Spacious Master Bedroom with access to covered Patio

■ This home is designed with a slab foundation

MAIN FLOOR — 3,254 SQ. FT.
GARAGE — 588 SQ. FT.

TOTAL LIVING AREA: 3,254 SQ. FT.

MAIN FLOOR

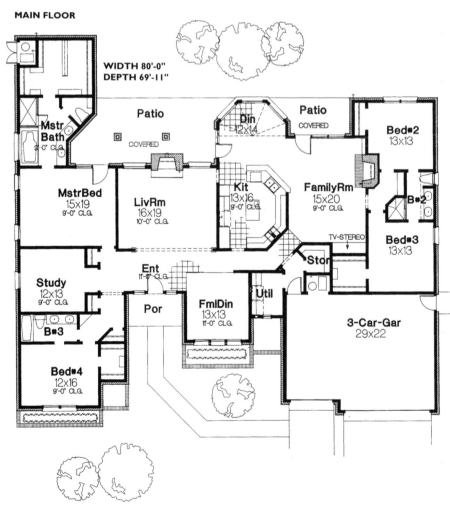

WIDTH 80'-0"
DEPTH 69'-11"

Split-Bedroom Privacy

Price Code: B

■ This plan features:

— Three bedrooms

— Two full baths

■ French doors flank the focal point fireplace in the Great Room and provide access to the backyard

■ The well-equipped Kitchen has a Pantry and large serving counter to the Dining Room

■ A third Garage bay offers ample storage and space for a possible workshop

■ This home is designed with a basement foundation

MAIN FLOOR — 1,755 SQ. FT.
BASEMENT — 1,725 SQ. FT.
GARAGE — 796 SQ. FT.

TOTAL LIVING AREA:
1,755 SQ. FT.

MAIN FLOOR

Dining
11'5" x 11'4"

Porch

Master Bedroom
17'2" x 12'

Great Room
23'9" x 17'

Kitchen
18' x 11'

Foyer

Three Car Garage
31'8" x 33'2"

Laun.

Bedroom
11'2" x 10'4"

Bedroom
12' x 10'4"

Porch

WIDTH 78'-6"
DEPTH 47'-7"

Discreet Garage

Price Code: B

■ This plan features:

— Three bedrooms

— Two full baths

■ The arched entrance and classic Porch provide a warm welcome

■ Ample counter space and a casual bar, separating the cooking area from the Dining Area, make an impressive Kitchen

■ The Dining Area is full of light, lined with windows, and open to the Great Room

■ Bedrooms fill the core of the right wing

■ A ceiling fan circulates the fresh air through the Screened Porch

■ This home is designed with a basement foundation

MAIN FLOOR — 1,611 SQ. FT.
GARAGE — 430 SQ. FT.

TOTAL LIVING AREA:
1,611 SQ. FT.

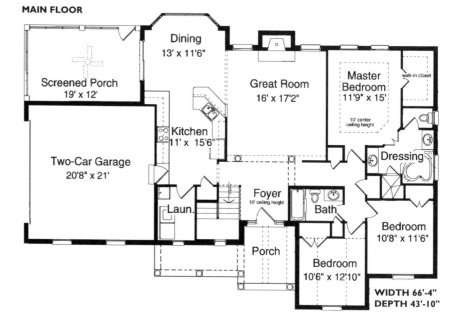

MAIN FLOOR

Dining 13' x 11'6"

Screened Porch 19' x 12'

Great Room 16' x 17'2"

Master Bedroom 11'9" x 15'

walk-in closet

Kitchen 11' x 15'6"

Two-Car Garage 20'8" x 21'

Dressing

10' center ceiling height

Laun.

Foyer 10' ceiling height

Bath

Porch

Bedroom 10'8" x 11'6"

Bedroom 10'6" x 12'10"

WIDTH 66'-4"
DEPTH 43'-10"

To order your Blueprints, call 1-800-235-5700

European Flavor

Price Code: C

■ This plan features:

— Three bedrooms

— Two full baths

■ A covered Entry reveals a Foyer with a 14-foot ceiling

■ The Family Room has a vaulted ceiling

■ The Breakfast Area has a tray ceiling and a bay of windows

■ The privately located Master Suite has a tray ceiling

■ This home is designed with basement and crawlspace foundation options

MAIN FLOOR — 1,779 SQ. FT.
BASEMENT — 1,818 SQ. FT.
GARAGE — 499 SQ. FT.

TOTAL LIVING AREA:
1,779 SQ. FT.

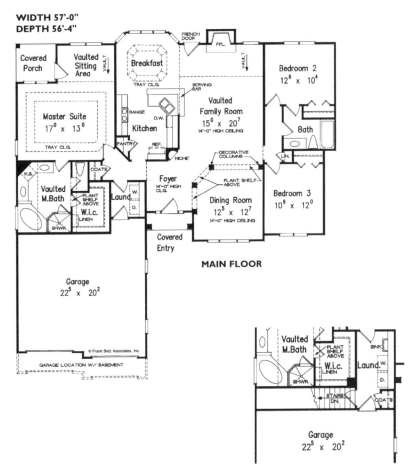

WIDTH 57'-0"
DEPTH 56'-4"

MAIN FLOOR

OPTIONAL BASEMENT
STAIR LOCATION

187

PLAN NO. 93722

MAIN FLOOR

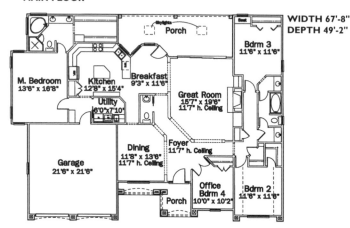

WIDTH 67'-8"
DEPTH 49'-2"

Adaptable Room

Price Code: D

- This plan features:
— Four bedrooms
— Two full and one half baths
- A front room conveniently located adjacent to the Foyer can be used as a home office or a Guest Room
- Skylights brighten the rear covered Porch
- Each of the secondary Bedrooms has access to a separate vanity; the Bedrooms share a tub
- This home is designed with basement, slab and crawlspace foundation options

MAIN FLOOR — 2,184 SQ. FT.
GARAGE — 462 SQ. FT.

TOTAL LIVING AREA:
2,184 SQ. FT.

PLAN NO. 98569

Courtyard Entrance

Price Code: G

- This plan features:
— Four bedrooms
— Two full, one three-quarter, and one half baths
- This home has a sophisticated air created by the courtyard entrance
- A large walk-in Pantry is located in the Breakfast Area for ample Kitchen storage
- The Master Bedroom has two walk-in closets and a luxurious Bath
- The future Playroom on the second floor will keep children's happy noises and toys away from view and earshot
- This home is designed with basement and slab foundation options

MAIN FLOOR — 2,911 SQ. FT.
GARAGE — 720 SQ. FT.

TOTAL LIVING AREA:
2,911 SQ. FT.

MAIN FLOOR

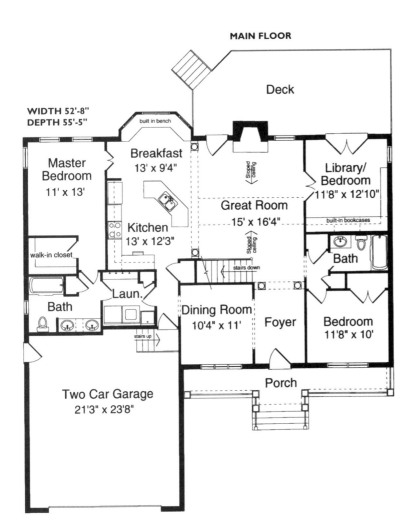

MAIN FLOOR

Deck

WIDTH 52'-8"
DEPTH 55'-5"

built in bench

Master
Bedroom
11' x 13'

Breakfast
13' x 9'4"

Library/
Bedroom
11'8" x 12'10"

Great Room
15' x 16'4"

Sloped ceiling

built-in bookcases

walk-in closet

Kitchen
13' x 12'3"

Sloped ceiling

stairs down

Bath

Laun.

Bath

stairs up

Dining Room
10'4" x 11'

Foyer

Bedroom
11'8" x 10'

Two Car Garage
21'3" x 23'8"

Porch

Library with Built-ins

Price Code: B

■ This plan features:

— Three bedrooms

— Two full baths

■ The built-in bench in the Breakfast Area offers space-saving seating for six

■ Double doors open to the Library, which features built-ins on two walls

■ The Great Room features a sloped ceiling and fireplace

■ This home is designed with a basement foundation

MAIN FLOOR — 1,594 SQ. FT.
BASEMENT — 1,594 SQ. FT.
GARAGE — 512 SQ. FT.

TOTAL LIVING AREA:
1,594 SQ. FT.

More Than Ceilings

Price Code A

■ This plan features:

— Three bedrooms

— Three full baths

■ Accent windows flank the chimney on the facade of the home

■ A cathedral ceiling in the Great Room and Dining Room adds grand scale

■ The bay window in the Dining Area creates an atmosphere for an exquisite formal experience

■ This home is designed with basement, slab, and crawlspace foundation options

■ Alternate foundation options available at an additional charge. Please call 1-800-235-5700 for more information.

MAIN FLOOR — 1,305 SQ. FT.
GARAGE — 418 SQ. FT.

TOTAL LIVING AREA:
1,305 SQ. FT.

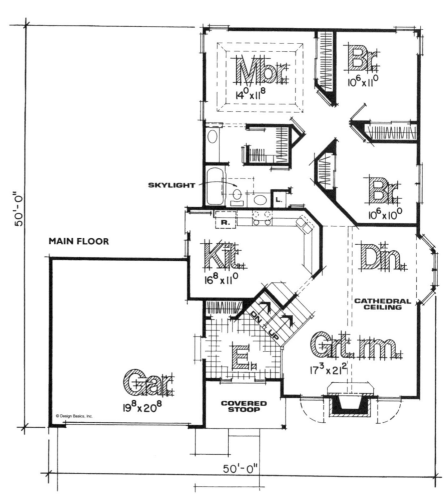

MAIN FLOOR

50'-0"

50'-0"

SKYLIGHT

Mbr
$14^0 \times 11^8$

Br
$10^6 \times 11^0$

Br
$10^6 \times 10^0$

L.

R.

Kit
$16^8 \times 11^0$

Dn
CATHEDRAL CEILING

Gar
$19^8 \times 20^8$

DN UP

Grt. rm.
$17^3 \times 21^2$

COVERED STOOP

© Design Basics, Inc.

To order your Blueprints, call 1-800-235-5700

WIDTH 65'-0"
DEPTH 68'-8"

MAIN FLOOR

FAMILY ROOM
15X17
CATHEDRAL CLG.

BOOK

BOOK

COVERED

PATIO AREA

BATH

BDRM. #4
13X10
9° CLG.

CLOS.

COVERED

BRKFT.
12X11
9° CLG.

COVERED
LANAI

MSTR.
BATH
9° CLG.

CLOS.

LIVING ROOM
13X13
12° CLG.

KIT.
12X13
9° CLG.

D.W.

OV.

W-I
CLOS.

SITTING
AREA

BDRM. #3
10X12
9° CLG.

HALL
9° CLG.

LINEN

REF

PANTRY

HALL
9° CLG.

MSTR. BDRM.
14X18
9° CLG.

CLOS.

GALLERY
11° CLG.

UTIL.

PWDR.

W. D.

BATH

LIN

ENT.
11° CLG.

FORMAL
DINING
11X13
11° CLG.

BDRM. #2
10X13
10° CLG.

POR.

THREE CAR
GARAGE

BOOK

Lap of Luxury

Price Code: E

■ This plan features:

— Four bedrooms

— Three full and one half baths

■ Entertaining in grand style in the formal Living Room, the Dining Room, or under the covered Patio in the backyard

■ Family Room crowned in a cathedral ceiling, enhanced by a center fireplace and built-in bookshelves

■ Master Bedroom with a Sitting Area, huge walk-in closet, private Bath and access to a covered Lanai

■ This home is designed with crawlspace and slab foundation options

MAIN FLOOR — 2,445 SQ. FT.
GARAGE — 630 SQ. FT.

TOTAL LIVING AREA:
2,445 SQ. FT.

Ranch of Distinction

Price Code: C

- This plan features:
- — Three bedrooms
- — Two full and one half baths
- The recessed entrance has an arched transom window over the door and a sidelight windows beside it
- Once inside the Living Room boasts a high ceiling and a warm fireplace
- The large Kitchen Area includes the open Dining Area with a rear bay that accessed the backyard
- The Master and third Bedrooms both have bay windows
- This home is designed with a basement foundation

MAIN FLOOR — 1,906 SQ. FT.
BASEMENT — 1,906 SQ. FT.

TOTAL LIVING AREA:
1,906 SQ. FT.

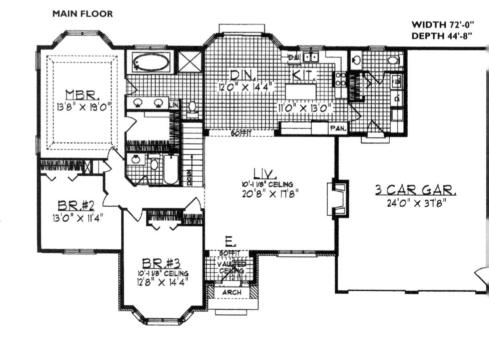

MAIN FLOOR

WIDTH 72'-0"
DEPTH 44'-8"

To order your Blueprints, call 1-800-235-5700

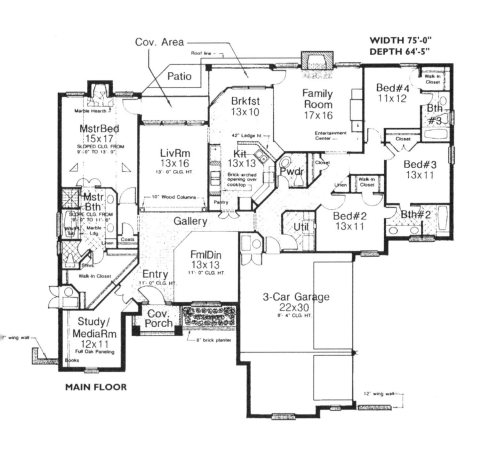

WIDTH 75'-0"
DEPTH 64'-5"

Cov. Area
Patio
Roof line
MstrBed 15x17
SLOPED CLG. FROM 9'-0" TO 13'-0"
Marble Hearth
LivRm 13x16
13'-0" CLG. HT
Brkfst 13x10
42" Ledge ht.
Kit 13x13
Brick-arched opening over cooktop
Pantry
Family Room 17x16
Entertainment Center
Bed#4 11x12
Walk-In Closet
Bth #3
Closet
Bed#3 13x11
Mstr Bth
SLOPE CLG. FROM 9'-0" TO 11'-0"
Whrlpl
Marble Ldg.
Linen
Coats
Shlvs.
10" Wood Columns
Gallery
Pwdr
Closet
Linen
Walk-In Closet
Util
Bed#2 13x11
Bth#2
Walk-In Closet
Entry 11'-0" CLG. HT.
FmlDin 13x13
11'-0" CLG. HT.
Study/ MediaRm 12x11
Full Oak Paneling
Books
Cov. Porch
6" brick planter
3-Car Garage 22x30
8'-4" CLG. HT.
2" wing wall
12" wing wall

MAIN FLOOR

Especially Unique

Price Code: F

■ This plan features:

— Four bedrooms

— Three full and one half baths

■ From the 11-foot Entry turn left into the Study/Media Room

■ The formal Dining Room is open to the Gallery, and the Living Room beyond

■ The Family Room has a built-in entertainment center, a fireplace and access to the rear Patio

■ The private Master Bedroom has a fireplace, a private Bath and a walk-in closet

■ This home is designed with a slab foundation

MAIN FLOOR — 2,748 SQ. FT.
GARAGE — 660 SQ. FT.

TOTAL LIVING AREA:
2,748 SQ. FT.

MAIN FLOOR

Three-Bedroom Ranch

Price Code: B

■ This plan features:

— Three bedrooms

— Two full baths

■ Formal Dining Room enhanced by a plant shelf and a side window

■ Wetbar located between the Kitchen and the Dining Room

■ Built-in Pantry, a double sink, and a serving bar highlight the Kitchen

■ Breakfast Room contains a radius window and a French door to the rear yard

■ Master Suite with a vaulted ceiling over the Sitting Room, a vaulted Master Bath and a walk-in closet

■ This home is designed with basement and crawlspace foundation options

MAIN FLOOR — 1,575 SQ. FT.

GARAGE — 459 SQ. FT.

TOTAL LIVING AREA:
1,575 SQ. FT.

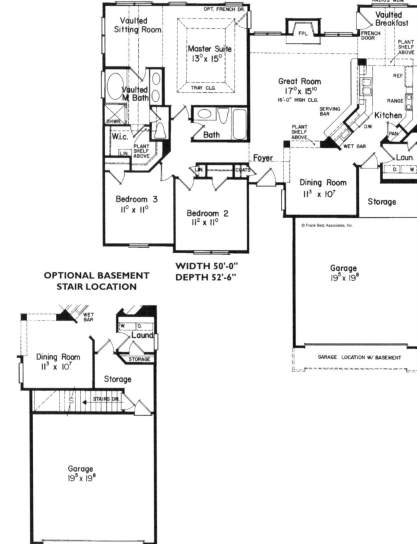

OPTIONAL BASEMENT
STAIR LOCATION

WIDTH 50'-0"
DEPTH 52'-6"

194

Contemporary Good Looks

Price Code: A

■ This plan features:
— Three bedrooms
— Two full baths

■ A vaulted Great Room provides space for the whole family

■ The covered Entry shelters guests at the door

■ Dine-in Breakfast Bar graces the Kitchen counter

■ The Master Suite benefits from a big walk-in closet

■ A nice sized Laundry leads off of the Kitchen

■ The Kitchen Pantry supplements already ample storage

■ This home is designed with basement, slab, and crawlspace foundation options

MAIN FLOOR — 1,433 SQ. FT.
BASEMENT — 1,433 SQ. FT.
GARAGE — 456 SQ. FT.

TOTAL LIVING AREA:
1,433 SQ. FT

PLAN NO. 96802

MAIN FLOOR

MAIN FLOOR W/O STAIRS OPTION

Split-Bedroom Layout

Price Code: C

■ This plan features:
— Four bedrooms
— Two full baths

■ A built-in next to the Great Room fireplace can store electronics

■ The Dining Room, located to the left of the Foyer, features two windows that view the front

■ The Garage has storage space for tools and gear

■ This home is designed with crawlspace and slab foundation options

MAIN FLOOR — 1,940 SQ. FT.
GARAGE — 417 SQ. FT.

TOTAL LIVING AREA:
1,940 SQ. FT.

PLAN NO. 82034

MAIN FLOOR

Unique V-Shaped Home

Price Code: I

■ This plan features:

— Two bedrooms

— Three full baths

■ Four skylights brighten the Eating Nook in the Country Kitchen

■ A walk-in Pantry, range-top work island, built-in barbecue and a sink add to the amenities of the Kitchen

■ Master Suite with his and hers closets and adjacent Dressing Area

■ A Guest Suite with a private Sitting Area and full Bath

■ This home is designed with a crawlspace foundation

Main floor — 3,417 sq. ft.
Garage — 795 sq. ft.

Total living area:
3,417 sq. ft.

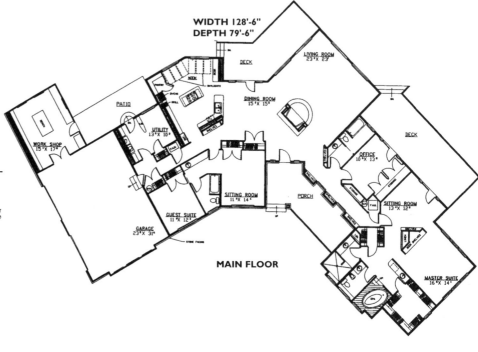

WIDTH 128'-6"
DEPTH 79'-6"

MAIN FLOOR

To order your Blueprints, call 1-800-235-5700

French Country Styling

Price Code: I

■ This plan features:

— Four bedrooms

— Three full and one half baths

■ Brick and stone blend masterfully for an impressive French Country exterior

■ Separate Master Suite with expansive Bath and closet

■ Study containing a built-in desk and bookcase

■ Angled island Kitchen highlighted by walk-in Pantry, and open to the Breakfast Bay

■ This home is designed with a slab foundation

MAIN FLOOR — 3,352 SQ. FT.
GARAGE — 672 SQ. FT.

TOTAL LIVING AREA:
3,352 SQ. FT.

WIDTH 91'-0"
DEPTH 71'-9"

MAIN FLOOR

MstrBed 16X17
LivRm 16X16
Mstr Bath
Study 12X11
Ent
FmlDin 12X13
Gallery
Kit 14X14
Brkfst 14X12'-6"
Patio Area
3-Car Garage
FmlyRm 18X18
Util
Bed#2 13X12
Bed#3 12X11
Bed#4 13X16

Plenty of Room

Price Code: A

- This plan features:
  — Three bedrooms
  — Two full baths
- The large Living Room features a corner fireplace
- The Master Bedroom, Dining Room and Living Room all feature an 11-foot high vaulted ceiling and views to the backyard
- Vaulted to 11-feet is the Kitchen, with an open bar view of the fireplace in the Living Room
- This home is designed with a slab foundation

MAIN FLOOR — 1,199 SQ. FT.
GARAGE — 484 SQ. FT.

TOTAL LIVING AREA:
1,199 SQ. FT.

WIDTH 44'-2"
DEPTH 42'-6.75"

MAIN FLOOR

Carefully Crafted Country

Price Code: A

- This plan features:
  — Three bedrooms
  — Two full baths
- Compact but complete, the Master Suite includes walk-in closet and 10-foot boxed ceiling
- Set into the Kitchen window, a cozy nook becomes just the place for an intimate meal
- Enjoy summer afternoon relaxing in the shade of your own front Porch
- The Laundry is convenient to the action-set into the hall between the two other Bedrooms
- Consider the third Bedroom as a potential Home Office or Library
- This home is designed with slab and crawlspace foundation options

MAIN FLOOR — 1,281 SQ. FT

TOTAL LIVING AREA:
1,281 SQ. FT.

WIDTH 44'-0"
DEPTH 54'-8"

MAIN FLOOR

To order your Blueprints, call 1-800-235-5700

46'-6"

TRAY CLG.

M. Bath

Master Suite
14° x 12°

W.i.c.

FPL.

VAULT

FRENCH
DOOR

Vaulted
Family Room
16 x 16⁵

SERVING
BAR

Breakfast

Kit.
RANGE

REF.

D

W.

PAN.

Bath

VAULT

COAT

LIN.

Storage

OPT. STAIRS
TO BASEMENT

Vaulted
Bedroom
10° x 10³

VAULT   VAULT

Bedroom
10° x 10°

Garage
19⁵ x 19⁹

41'-0"

MAIN FLOOR

© Frank Betz Associates, Inc.

GARAGE LOCATION W/BASEMENT

Decorative Ceilings

Price Code: A

■ This plan features:

— Three bedrooms

— Two full baths

■ The Family Room has a vaulted ceiling, a corner fireplace, and a French door to the rear yard

■ The Breakfast Book is brightened by window on two of its walls

■ The Master Suite has a tray ceiling, a walk in closet and a private Bath

■ This home is designed with basement, slab, and crawlspace foundation options

MAIN FLOOR — 1,104 SQ. FT.
BASEMENT — 1,104 SQ. FT.
GARAGE — 400 SQ. FT.

TOTAL LIVING AREA:
1,104 SQ. FT.

Outstanding Four Bedroom

Price Code: C

■ This plan features:

— Four bedrooms

— Two full baths

■ Radius window highlighting the exterior and the formal Dining Room

■ High ceiling topping the Foyer for a grand first impression

■ Vaulted ceiling enhancing the Great Room accented by a fireplace framed by windows

■ Breakfast Room topped by a vaulted ceiling and enhanced by elegant French door to the rear yard

■ Tray ceiling and a compartmental Bath gives luxurious presence to the Master Suite

■ This home is designed with basement and crawlspace foundation options

MAIN FLOOR — 1,945 SQ. FT.

TOTAL LIVING AREA:
1,945 SQ. FT.

MAIN FLOOR

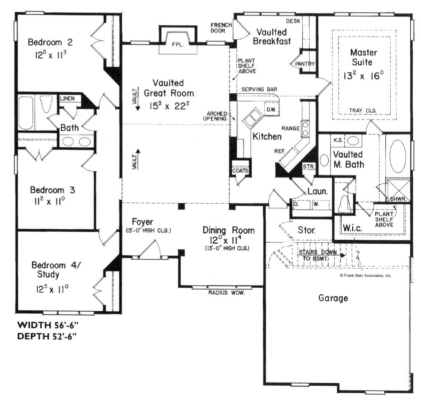

WIDTH 56'-6"
DEPTH 52'-6"

200

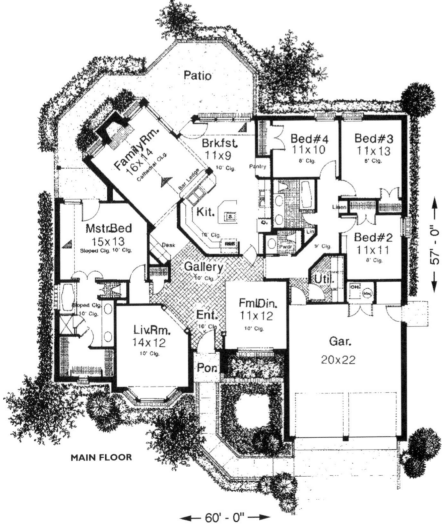

MAIN FLOOR

← 60' - 0" →

57' - 0"

Stunning Family Plan

Price Code: D

■ This plan features:

— Four bedrooms

— Two full and one half baths

■ Windows, brick, and columns combine to create an eye-catching elevation

■ A pair of columns greets you as you enter the Living Room

■ The formal Dining Room is located just steps away from the Kitchen

■ Set away from the active areas the Master Bedroom is a quiet retreat

■ This home is designed with a slab foundation

MAIN FLOOR — 2,194 SQ. FT.
GARAGE — 462 SQ. FT.

TOTAL LIVING AREA:
2,194 SQ. FT.

One Floor Living

Price Code: A

■ This plan features:

— Three bedrooms

— Two full baths

■ A covered front Porch is supported by graceful columns

■ The Living Room features a cozy fireplace and a ceiling fan

■ The Kitchen is distinguished by an angled serving bar

■ The Dining Room is convenient to the Kitchen and the rear Porch

■ The Master Bedroom has a walk-in closet and a private Bath

■ A two-car Garage with storage space is located in the rear of the home

■ This home is designed with crawlspace and slab foundation options

MAIN FLOOR — 1,247 SQ. FT.
GARAGE — 512 SQ. FT.

TOTAL LIVING AREA:
1,247 SQ. FT.

MAIN FLOOR

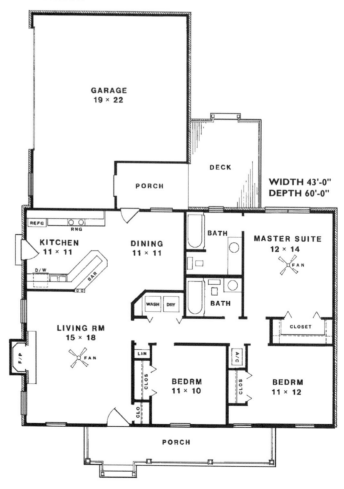

WIDTH 43'-0"
DEPTH 60'-0"

To order your Blueprints, call 1-800-235-5700

Quaint and Cozy

Price Code: B

■ This plan features:
— Three bedrooms
— Two full baths
■ The luxurious Master Suite includes two walk-in closets, a linen closet, plus a Sitting Room
■ Living space extends to a skylit screen Porch and Deck beyond
■ The Great Room features a volume ceiling and focal point fireplace
■ This home is designed with basement and crawlspace foundation options

MAIN FLOOR — 1,787 SQ. FT.
BONUS ROOM — 263 SQ. FT.

TOTAL LIVING AREA:
1,787 SQ. FT.

Great Room Accesses Grilling Porch

Price Code: C

■ This plan features
— Three bedrooms
— Two full baths
■ The bay window in the Breakfast Area brightens the adjacent Kitchen
■ A closet in the Garage stores tools and seasonal equipment
■ The Master Bedroom has a private Bath with a walk-in closet
■ This home is designed with basement, slab, and crawlspace foundation options

MAIN FLOOR — 1,787 SQ. FT
GARAGE — 417 SQ. FT

TOTAL LIVING AREA:
1,787 SQ. FT.

PLAN NO. 98469

Rambling Ranch

Price Code: C

- This plan features:
  — Three bedrooms
  — Two full baths
- The Living Room is complemented by a vaulted ceiling, a corner fireplace, and a plant shelf
- The galley Kitchen is fully equipped and the entry to the Laundry Room is at it's far end
- There are two secondary Bedrooms located in the front of the home, they share a full Bath
- This home is designed with basement and crawl-space foundation options

MAIN FLOOR — 1,042 SQ. FT.
BASEMENT — 1,042 SQ. FT.
GARAGE — 400 SQ. FT.

TOTAL LIVING AREA:
1,042 SQ. FT.

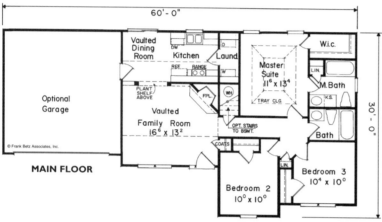

MAIN FLOOR

PLAN NO. 92247

Looks Like You've Arrived

Price Code: D

- This plan features:
  — Four bedrooms
  — Two full and one half baths
- The built-in Pantry and abundant storage and counter space add to the Kitchen's efficiency
- Look up to the nearly 10-foot tall vaulted ceiling in the Master Bedroom
- The convenient Laundry features liberal built-ins
- One full wing of this home is a suite of two Bedrooms connected by a Bath with separate vanities
- This home was designed with a slab foundation

MAIN FLOOR — 2,149 SQ. FT
GARAGE — 465 SQ. FT.

TOTAL LIVING AREA:
2,149 SQ. FT.

MAIN FLOOR

WIDTH 55'-0"
DEPTH 64'-10"

204

To order your Blueprints, call 1-800-235-5700

Stately Columns
Create A Classic

Price Code: A

■ This plan features:
– Two bedrooms
– Two full baths
■ Compact layout of this home is perfect for empty-nesters
■ The second Bedroom can also double as a Study or Home Office
■ Kitchen, Dining Room and Living Room combine in an open plan
■ For informal dining, a Breakfast Bar adjoins the Kitchen counter
■ Extra tall ceilings grace the Dining and Living Rooms
■ This home is designed with crawlspace and slab foundation options

MAIN FLOOR — 1,172 SQ. FT.
GARAGE — 213 SQ. FT.

TOTAL LIVING AREA:
1,172 SQ. FT.

MAIN FLOOR

Complete Efficiency

Price Code: A

■ This plan features:
– Three bedrooms
– Two full baths
■ Though only 30-feet wide, this narrow-lot home includes a full double Garage
■ A large Family Room, Kitchen and Dining Room are among the full-size spaces in this home
■ An interior Laundry is centrally located between Kitchen and Bedrooms
■ The rear-placed Master Suite is spacious and complete
■ This home was designed with a slab foundation

MAIN FLOOR — 1,284 SQ. FT.
GARAGE — 375 SQ. FT.

TOTAL LIVING AREA:
1,284 SQ. FT.

WIDTH 30'-0"
DEPTH 60'-10"

MAIN FLOOR

To order your Blueprints, call 1-800-235-5700

Angled Elegance

Price Code: A

- This plan features:
- — Three bedrooms
- — Two full baths
- Cathedral and sloped ceilings characterize this family-friendly floor plan
- A fireplace with raised hearth and a built-in media cabinet enhance the Living Room
- The Dining Room and Master Bedroom overlook the Patio and backyard
- This home is designed with a slab foundation

MAIN FLOOR — 1,431 SQ. FT.
GARAGE — 410 SQ. FT.

TOTAL LIVING AREA:
1,431 SQ. FT.

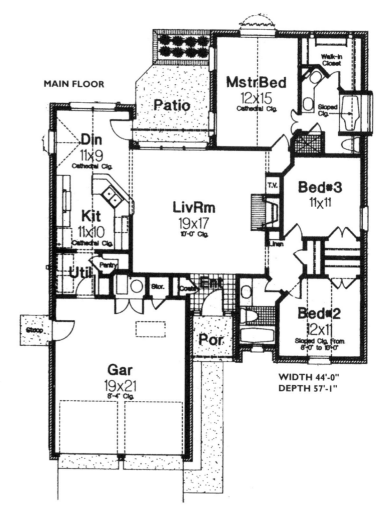

MAIN FLOOR

Patio

MstrBed
12x15
Cathedral Clg.

Walk-In Closet

Sloped Clg.

Din
11x9
Cathedral Clg.

LivRm
19x17
10'-0" Clg.

T.V.

Bed#3
11x11

Kit
11x10
Cathedral Clg.

Linen

Util

Pantry

Stor.

Coat

Ent

Bed#2
12x11
Sloped Clg. From 8'-0" to 10'-0"

Stoop

Por.

Gar
19x21
8'-4" Clg.

WIDTH 44'-0"
DEPTH 57'-1"

Country Kitchen

Price Code: D

- This plan features:
  - Four bedrooms
  - Two full baths
- The Kitchen is open to an informal Dining Room with French doors that seclude it from the Entry
- The front Porch and rear Patio offer space for outdoor entertaining or relaxation
- The Master Bedroom has a vaulted ceiling and access to the Covered Patio
- This home is designed with crawlspace and slab foundation options

MAIN FLOOR — 2,078 SQ. FT.

GARAGE — 734 SQ. FT.

TOTAL LIVING AREA:
2,078 SQ. FT.

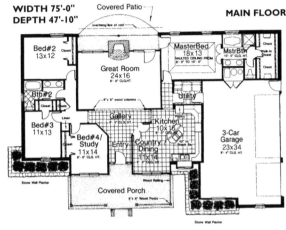

WIDTH 75'-0"
DEPTH 47'-10"

MAIN FLOOR

Perfect Use of Space

Price Code: B

- This plan features:
  - Three bedrooms
  - Two full baths
- A large Family Room, with fireplace, anchors this well-designed home
- The Porch off the Family Room offers space for backyard barbecues
- You'll fall in love with the Master Suite
- An unfinished basement offers a world of future growth options
- This home is designed with crawlspace and basement foundation options

MAIN FLOOR — 1,708 SQ. FT.

GARAGE — 544 SQ. FT.

TOTAL LIVING AREA:
1,708 SQ. FT

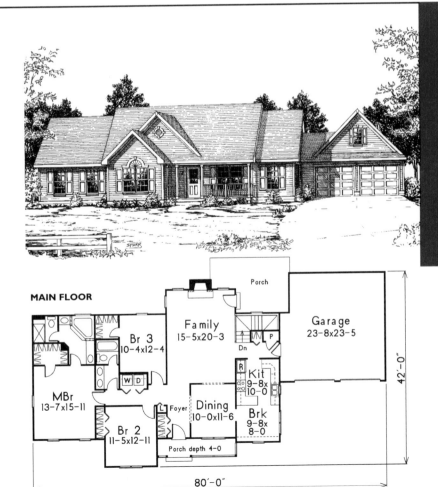

MAIN FLOOR

To order your Blueprints, call 1-800-235-5700

A Garage Designed for Golfers

Price Code: A

■ This plan features:
— Three bedrooms
— Two full baths
■ The Garage contains two full auto bays plus a golf cart Bay
■ Whirlpool and glassed-in shower round out the Master Bath
■ A covered Porch off the Breakfast Room provides an outdoor eating area
■ There's plenty of storage space throughout this home
■ This home is designed with crawlspace and slab foundation options

MAIN FLOOR — 1,379 SQ. FT.
GARAGE — 493 SQ. FT.

TOTAL LIVING AREA:
1,379 SQ. FT.

MAIN FLOOR

WIDTH 38'-4"
DEPTH 68'-6"

Fit for the Whole Family

Price Code: C

■ This plan features:
— Four bedrooms
— Two full baths
■ Use the front Bedroom as a Guest Room or turn it into your Home Office or Study
■ The vaulted ceiling, walk-in closet and complete Bath spell Master Suite luxury
■ A wraparound counter and center island make the most of every square foot of Kitchen space
■ Got a riding lawnmower? Use the 55 sq. ft. of extra storage in the two-car Garage
■ Watch the neighbors walk by from your covered front Porch or relax in privacy on the covered Patio
■ This home comes with a basement foundation

MAIN FLOOR — 1,791 SQ. FT
BASEMENT — 1,791 SQ. FT.

TOTAL LIVING AREA:
1,791 SQ. FT.

MAIN FLOOR

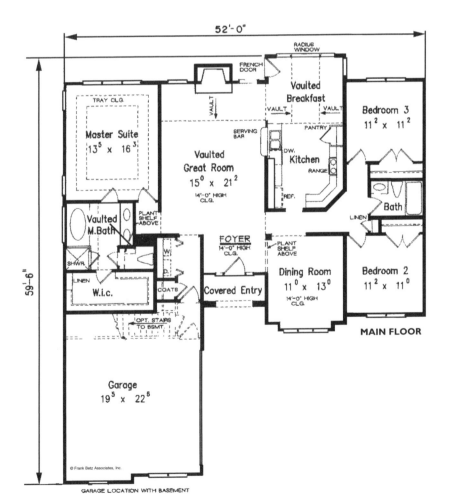

52'-0"

59'-6"

RADIUS WINDOW

FRENCH DOOR

TRAY CLG.

Master Suite
13⁵ x 16³

Vaulted
M.Bath

PLANT SHELF ABOVE

SHWR.

LINEN

W.i.c.

COATS

OPT. STAIRS TO BSMT.

Garage
19³ x 22⁸

GARAGE LOCATION WITH BASEMENT

© Frank Betz Associates, Inc.

Vaulted Great Room
15⁰ x 21²
14'-0" HIGH CLG.

VAULT

SERVING BAR

Vaulted Breakfast

VAULT   VAULT

Kitchen

D.W.

RANGE

REF.

PANTRY

Bedroom 3
11² x 11²

Bath

LINEN

FOYER
14'-0" HIGH CLG.

PLANT SHELF ABOVE

Covered Entry

Dining Room
11⁰ x 13⁰
14'-0" HIGH CLG.

Bedroom 2
11² x 11⁰

MAIN FLOOR

Charming Stucco

Price Code: B

■ This plan features:

— Three bedrooms

— Two full baths

■ Attractive entrance with curved transom and side lights

■ A vaulted ceiling above the Great Room and Breakfast Room

■ Cozy fireplace with windows to either side in the Great Room

■ Tray ceiling crowning the Master Bedroom and a vaulted ceiling over the plush Master Bath

■ This home is designed with basement and crawlspace foundation options

MAIN FLOOR — 1,696 SQ. FT.
GARAGE — 475 SQ. FT.
BASEMENT — 1,720 SQ. FT.

TOTAL LIVING AREA:
1,696 SQ. FT.

MAIN FLOOR

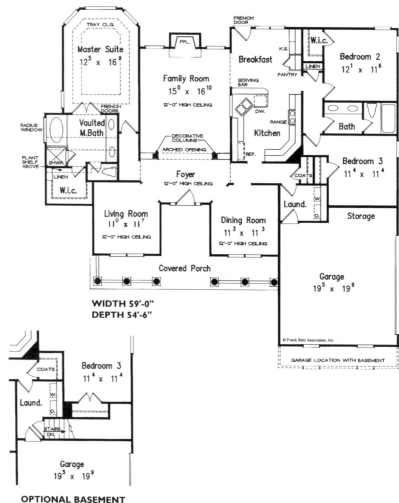

Covered Porch with Columns

Price Code: C

■ This plan features:

— Three bedrooms

— Two full baths

■ Foyer with 12-foot ceiling leads into the Family Room which has a focal point fireplace

■ Living Room and Dining Room overlook the front Porch

■ Kitchen has a serving bar, Breakfast Area and a French door that opens to the backyard

■ This home is designed with basement, slab, and crawlspace foundation options

MAIN FLOOR — 1,856 SQ. FT.
BASEMENT — 1,856 SQ. FT.
GARAGE — 429 SQ. FT.

TOTAL LIVING AREA:
1,856 SQ. FT.

To order your Blueprints, call 1-800-235-5700

MAIN FLOOR

ENT. CENTER

Hrth
10⁰x14⁰

TRANS.

Bfst.
10⁰x10³

SNACK BAR

Mbr.
13⁰x15⁵

9'-4" CEILING

OPTIONAL DEN

Br.
12⁰x11²

Grt. rm.
16³x22⁸

Kit.
13⁰x10⁶

WHIRLPOOL

SKYLIGHT

10'-0" CEILING

DN

SKYLIGHT

W D

Br.
12⁰x11³

E

Dn.
12⁰x13⁰

12'-0" CLG.

LIN.

COVERED STOOP

Gar.
21⁴x21⁸

© Design Basics, Inc.

58'-0"

56'-0"

Beautiful Arched Window

Price Code: C

- ■ This plan features:
- —Three bedrooms
- —Two full baths
- ■ 10-foot ceilings top the Entry and the Great Room
- ■ Breakfast Room and Hearth Room are in an open layout and share a see-through fireplace
- ■ Split-Bedroom plan assures homeowner's privacy in the Master Suite
- ■ This home is designed with a basement foundation
- ■ Alternate foundation options available at an additional charge. Please call 1-800-235-5700 for more information.

MAIN FLOOR — 1,911 SQ. FT.
GARAGE — 481 SQ. FT.

TOTAL LIVING AREA:
1,911 SQ. FT.

Open Spaces

Price Code: A

■ This plan features:

— Three bedrooms

— Two full baths

■ Open floor plan between the Family Room and the Dining Room

■ Vaulted ceilings adding volume and a fireplace in the Family Room

■ Three Bedrooms; the Master Suite with a five-piece private Bath

■ Convenient Laundry Center located outside the Bedrooms

■ This home is designed with a crawl-space foundation

MAIN FLOOR — 1,135 SQ. FT.
GARAGE — 460 SQ. FT.

TOTAL LIVING AREA:
1,135 SQ. FT.

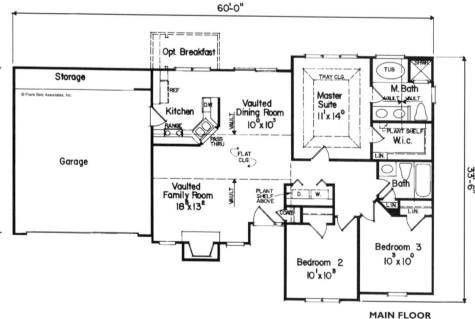

MAIN FLOOR

To order your Blueprints, call 1-800-235-5700

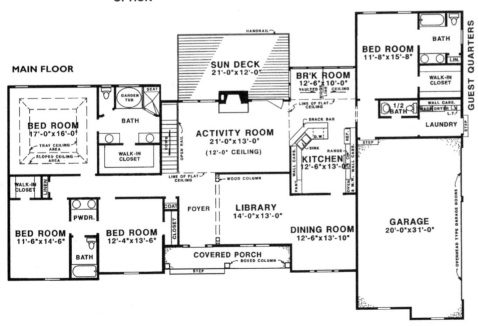

WHEELCHAIR BATH OPTION

MAIN FLOOR

SUN DECK 21'-0"x12'-0"

HANDRAIL

GARDEN TUB   SEAT

BED ROOM 17'-0"x16'-0"
TRAY CEILING AREA
SLOPED CEILING AREA

BATH

WALK-IN CLOSET

OPEN RAIL

ACTIVITY ROOM 21'-0"x13'-0" (12'-0" CEILING)

LINE OF FLAT CEILING

WOOD COLUMN

BR'K ROOM 12'-6"x10'-0" VAULTED CEILING

LINE OF FLAT CEILING

SNACK BAR
D.W.
SINK
KITCHEN 12'-6"x13'-0"
RANGE
PANT.
REF.
OVEN & M.W.
WALL CABS.

BED ROOM 11'-8"x15'-8"

BATH
LIN.

WALK-IN CLOSET

1/2 BATH
WALL CABS.
WASH DRYER
L.T.
LAUNDRY

GUEST QUARTERS

STEP

WALK-IN CLOSET
LINEN

PWDR.

BED ROOM 11'-6"x14'-6"
BATH

COAT
CLOSET

FOYER

LIBRARY 14'-0"x13'-0"

BED ROOM 12'-4"x13'-6"

COVERED PORCH
STEP
BOXED COLUMN

DINING ROOM 12'-6"x13'-10"

GARAGE 20'-0"x31'-0"

OVERHEAD TYPE GARAGE DOORS

STEP

Stone and Siding

Price Code: F

■ This plan features:
— Four bedrooms
— Three full and one half baths

■ Attractive styling and a covered Porch create curb appeal

■ Formal Foyer giving access to the Bedroom wing, Library or Activity Room

■ A snack bar/peninsula counter highlights the Kitchen which also contains a built-in Pantry

■ Master Suite topped by a tray ceiling and pampered by five-piece Bath

■ This home is designed with a basement foundation

MAIN FLOOR — 2,690 SQ. FT.
BASEMENT — 2,690 SQ. FT.
GARAGE — 660 SQ. FT.
DECK — 252 SQ. FT.

TOTAL LIVING AREA:
2,690 SQ. FT.

Columned Keystone Arched Entry

Price Code: E

■ This plan features:

— Three bedrooms

— Two full baths

■ Keystone arches and arched transoms above the windows

■ Formal Dining Room and Study flank the Foyer

■ Fireplace in Great Room

■ Efficient Kitchen with a peninsula counter and bayed Nook

■ A step ceiling in the Master Suite and interesting Master Bath with a triangular area for the oval bath tub

■ This home is designed with slab and crawlspace foundation options

MAIN FLOOR — 2,256 SQ. FT.
GARAGE — 514 SQ. FT.

TOTAL LIVING AREA:
2,256 SQ. FT.

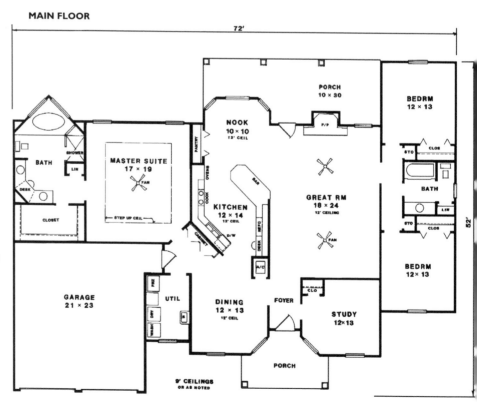

MAIN FLOOR

To order your Blueprints, call 1-800-235-5700

WIDTH 60'-6"
DEPTH 56'-0"

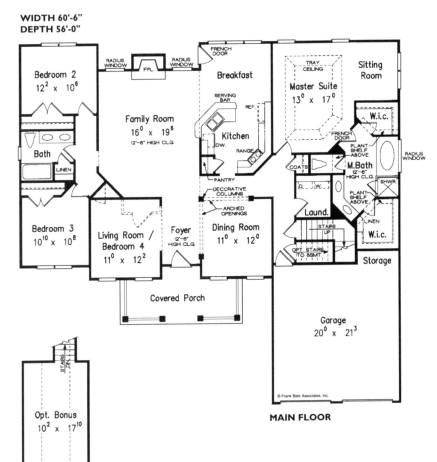

MAIN FLOOR

BONUS

Stately Front Porch with Columns

Price Code: D

■ This plan features:

— Three bedrooms

— Two full baths

■ Tray ceiling crowning Master Bedroom highlighted by a Sitting Room

■ Arched openings accented by columns accessing the formal Dining Room

■ This home is designed with basement and crawlspace foundation options

MAIN FLOOR — 2,056 SQ. FT.
GARAGE — 454 SQ. FT.
BONUS — 208 SQ. FT.
BASEMENT — 2,056 SQ. FT.

TOTAL LIVING AREA:
2,056 SQ. FT.

Backyard Views

Price Code: B

■ This plan features:

— Three bedrooms

— Two full baths

■ Front Porch accesses open Foyer, and spacious Dining Room and Great Room with sloped ceilings

■ Corner fireplace, windows and atrium door to Patio enhance Great Room

■ Convenient Kitchen with a Pantry and a peninsula serving counter

■ Luxurious Bath, walk-in closet and backyard view offered in Master Bedroom

■ This home is designed with a basement foundation

MAIN FLOOR — 1,746 SQ. FT.
GARAGE — 480 SQ. FT.
BASEMENT — 1,697 SQ. FT.

TOTAL LIVING AREA:
1,746 SQ. FT.

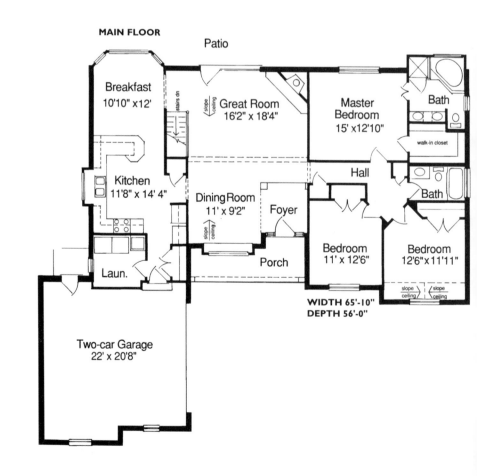

MAIN FLOOR

Patio

Breakfast
10'10" x12'

Great Room
16'2" x 18'4"

Master Bedroom
15' x12'10"

Bath

walk-in closet

Kitchen
11'8" x 14' 4"

Dining Room
11' x 9'2"

Foyer

Hall

Bath

stairs dn

slope ceiling

slope ceiling

Bedroom
11' x 12'6"

Bedroom
12'6"x 11'11"

Porch

Laun.

slope ceiling

slope ceiling

WIDTH 65'-10"
DEPTH 56'-0"

Two-car Garage
22' x 20'8"

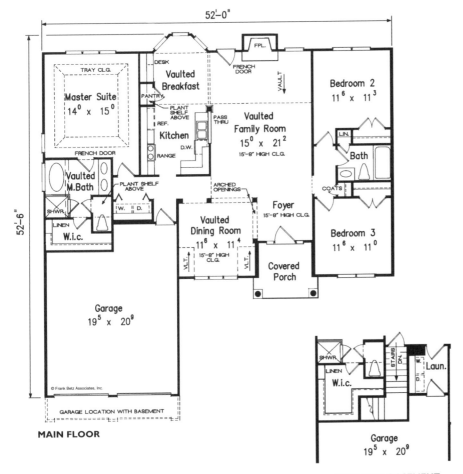

MAIN FLOOR

52'-0"

TRAY CLG.

Master Suite
14⁰ x 15⁰

FRENCH DOOR

DESK

Vaulted
Breakfast

PANTRY

PLANT
SHELF
ABOVE

REF.

Kitchen

RANGE

D.W.

PASS
THRU

FPL.

FRENCH
DOOR

VAULT

Vaulted
Family Room
15⁰ x 21²
15'-8" HIGH CLG.

Bedroom 2
11⁶ x 11³

LIN.

Bath

COATS

Vaulted
M.Bath

PLANT SHELF
ABOVE

W. II D.

SHWR.

LINEN

W.i.c.

ARCHED
OPENINGS

Vaulted
Dining Room
11⁶ x 11⁴
15'-8" HIGH
CLG.

VLT.

VLT.

Foyer
15'-8" HIGH CLG.

Covered
Porch

Bedroom 3
11⁶ x 11⁰

52'-6"

Garage
19⁵ x 20⁹

© Frank Betz Associates, Inc.

GARAGE LOCATION WITH BASEMENT

SHWR.

LINEN

W.i.c.

STAIRS

DN.

W. D.

Laun.

Garage
19⁵ x 20⁹

**OPTIONAL BASEMENT
STAIR LOCATION**

Attention to Details

Price Code: B

■ This plan features:

— Three bedrooms

— Two full baths

■ Foyer, Family Room and Dining Room have 15'8" ceilings

■ Split-Bedroom floor plan, affording additional privacy to the Master Suite

■ Master Suite enhanced by a tray ceiling, a five-piece Master Bath and a walk-in closet

■ This home is designed with basement and crawlspace foundation options

MAIN FLOOR — 1,575 SQ. FT
BASEMENT — 1,612 SQ. FT.
GARAGE — 456 SQ. FT.

TOTAL LIVING AREA:
1,575 SQ. FT.

Hip Roof Ranch

Price Code: B

- ■ This plan features:
- — Three bedrooms
- — Two full baths
- ■ Cozy front Porch leads into Entry with vaulted ceiling and sidelights
- ■ Open Living Room enhanced by a cathedral ceiling, a wall of windows and corner fireplace
- ■ Large and efficient Kitchen with an extended counter and a bright Dining Area with access to Screen Porch
- ■ Convenient Utility Area with access to Garage and Storage Area
- ■ This home is designed with a basement foundation

MAIN FLOOR — 1,540 SQ. FT.
BASEMENT — 1,540 SQ. FT.

TOTAL LIVING AREA:
1,540 SQ. FT.

MAIN FLOOR

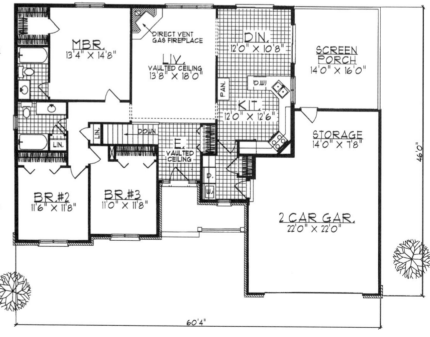

To order your Blueprints, call 1-800-235-5700

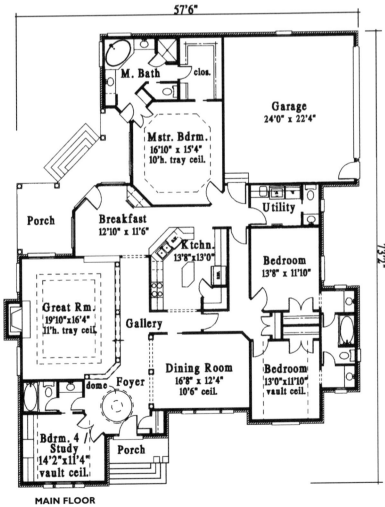

57'6"

M. Bath

clos.

Garage
24'0" x 22'4"

Mstr. Bdrm.
16'10" x 15'4"
10'h. tray ceil.

Porch

Breakfast
12'10" x 11'6"

Utility

Ktchn.
13'8"x13'0"

73'2"

Bedroom
13'8" x 11'10"

Great Rm.
19'10"x16'4"
11'h. tray ceil.

Gallery

Dining Room
16'8" x 12'4"
10'6" ceil.

Bedroom
13'0"x11'10"
vault ceil.

dome   Foyer

Bdrm. 4
Study
14'2"x11'4"
vault ceil.

Porch

MAIN FLOOR

Tailored for a View to the Side

Price Code: F

■ This plan features:

— Three bedrooms

— Three full and one half baths

■ Entry Foyer highlighted by a ceiling dome and French doors leading to the private Study

■ Elegant formal Dining Room with a high ceiling, columns and arched entrance

■ Sunken Great Room with a high tray ceiling, arched openings with columns and a fireplace

■ An island and walk-in Pantry add to the Kitchen's efficiency

■ This home is designed with slab and crawlspace foundation options

MAIN FLOOR — 2,579 SQ. FT.
GARAGE — 536 SQ. FT.

TOTAL LIVING AREA:
2,579 SQ. FT.

Pleasant and Practical

Price Code: B

- This plan features:
— Three bedrooms
— Two full baths
- A tray ceiling and columns enhance the open design of the formal Dining Room
- The Living Room's corner fireplace creates a warm and welcoming spot
- The Master Suite, with generous walk-in closet and luxurious Bath, is isolated for privacy in the left wing
- This home is designed with a crawlspace foundation

MAIN FLOOR — 1,589 SQ. FT.
GARAGE — 481 SQ. FT.

TOTAL LIVING AREA:
1,589 SQ. FT.

WIDTH 59'-10"
DEPTH 57'-9"

MAIN FLOOR

Mbr 12-8 × 14-8
Liv 16 × 16
Brk 9-2 × 9-2
Kit 10 × 10
Din 11-4 × 15-0 Tray Ceiling
Br #2 11-4 × 10-4
Br #3 11-4 × 10-4
Gar 20 × 23
Porch
Clo
Bath
Entry
Stor

Setting the Standard

Price Code: D

- This plan features:
— Four bedrooms
— Two full baths
- A row of clerestory windows in the dormer bathes the Great Room in natural light
- Enjoy the Study or use it as a Guest Room or Nursery
- This liberally laid-out Kitchen has it all, including a nearby Laundry
- A corner fireplace in the Great Room offers a cozy view in all directions
- Just off the Master Suite, the small Porch offers intimate relaxation
- This home is designed with a basement foundation

MAIN FLOOR — 2,029 SQ. FT
GARAGE — 431 SQ. FT.

TOTAL LIVING AREA:
2,029 SQ. FT

61'-0"
51'-0"

MAIN FLOOR

Br 3 11-0x12-0
Study 10-8x 12-0
Patio
Garage 22-10x20-1
Great Room 20-1x19-5 vaulted clg plant shelf
Br 2 11-0x10-0
Kit/Dining 20-0x18-11
Entry
MBr 17-4x14-0 vaulted clg
Porch
Porch depth 6-0

To order your Blueprints, call 1-800-235-5700

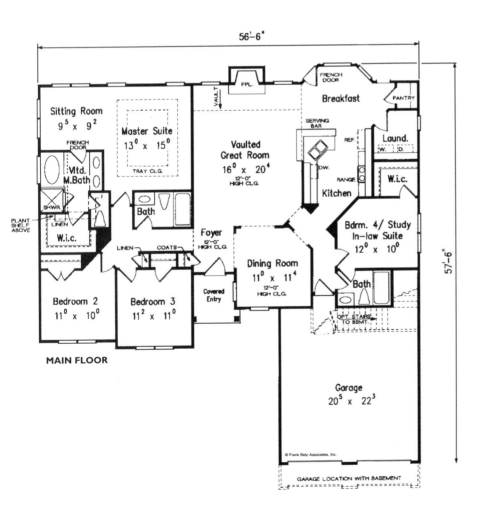

56'-6"

57'-6"

Sitting Room
9⁵ x 9²

FRENCH DOOR

Master Suite
13⁰ x 15⁰
TRAY CLG.

FPL

VAULT

FRENCH DOOR

Breakfast

PANTRY

Mtd. M.Bath

SHWR.

PLANT SHELF ABOVE

LINEN

W.i.c.

Bath

Vaulted Great Room
16⁰ x 20⁴
12'-0" HIGH CLG.

Kitchen

SERVING BAR

REF.

DW.

RANGE

Laund.
W. D.

W.i.c.

LINEN

COATS

Foyer
12'-0" HIGH CLG.

Dining Room
11⁰ x 11⁴
12'-0" HIGH CLG.

Bdrm. 4/ Study In-law Suite
12⁰ x 10⁰

Bedroom 2
11⁰ x 10⁰

Bedroom 3
11² x 11⁰

Covered Entry

Bath

OPT. STAIRS TO BSMT.

MAIN FLOOR

Garage
20⁵ x 22³

© Frank Betz Associates, Inc.

GARAGE LOCATION WITH BASEMENT

Exquisite Master Suite

Price Code: C

■ This plan features:

— Four Bedrooms

— Three full baths

■ Formal Foyer with a convenient coat closet

■ Vaulted ceiling over the Great Room highlighted by a fireplace flanked by windows

■ Cozy Breakfast Bay with French door to rear yard

■ Master Suite pampered by private Sitting Room and luxurious Master Bath

■ This home is designed with basement and crawlspace foundation options

MAIN FLOOR — 1,915 SQ. FT.
GARAGE — 489 SQ. FT.
BASEMENT — 1,932 SQ. FT.

TOTAL LIVING AREA:
1,915 SQ. FT.

No Wasted Space

Price Code: A

■ This plan features:

— Three bedrooms

— Two full baths

■ A centrally located Great Room with a cathedral ceiling, exposed wood beams, and large areas of fixed glass

■ The Living and Dining areas separated by a massive stone fireplace

■ A secluded Master Suite with a walk-in closet and private Master Bath

■ An efficient Kitchen with a convenient Laundry Area

■ This home is designed with basement, slab, and crawlspace foundation options

MAIN FLOOR— 1,454 SQ. FT.

TOTAL LIVING AREA:
1,454 SQ. FT.

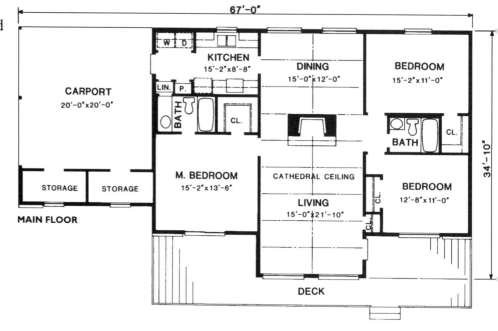

67'-0"

CARPORT
20'-0"x20'-0"

W D

KITCHEN
15'-2"x8'-8"

LIN.   P.

BATH

CL.

DINING
15'-0"x12'-0"

BEDROOM
15'-2"x11'-0"

BATH

CL.

STORAGE   STORAGE

M. BEDROOM
15'-2"x13'-6"

CATHEDRAL CEILING

LIVING
15'-0"x21'-10"

CL.

BEDROOM
12'-8"x11'-0"

CL.

34'-10"

MAIN FLOOR

DECK

Work Comfortably in Your Home Office

Price Code: D

■ This plan features:

— Three bedrooms

— Two full baths

■ The Entry leads directly into the formal Dining Room or the Great Room, and is ideal for guest traffic

■ The Office has its own private entrance and bump-out window

■ Counter space is abundant in the U-shaped Kitchen and adds convenience and practicality to preparing meals

■ The Master Suite features a roomy walk-in closet and luxurious Bath

■ This home is designed with a basement foundation

■ Alternate foundation options available at an additional charge. Please call 1-800-235-5700 for more information.

MAIN FLOOR — 2,151 SQ. FT.

TOTAL LIVING AREA:
2,151 SQ. FT.

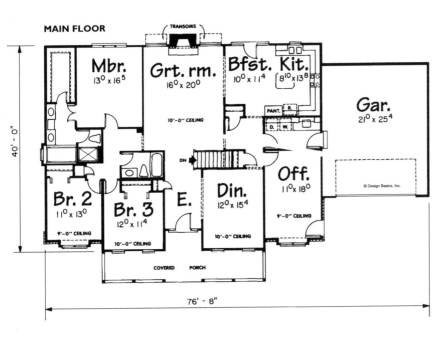

MAIN FLOOR

Mbr.
13⁰ x 16⁵

Grt. rm.
16⁰ x 20⁰
10'-0" CEILING

Bfst.
10⁰ x 11⁴

Kit.
8¹⁰ x 13⁸

Gar.
21⁰ x 25⁴

PANT.

R.

D. W.

Br. 2
11⁰ x 13⁰
9'-0" CEILING

Br. 3
12⁰ x 11⁴
10'-0" CEILING

E.

DN

Din.
12⁰ x 15⁴
10'-0" CEILING

Off.
11⁰ x 18⁰
9'-0" CEILING

© Design Basics, Inc.

TRANSOMS

40'-0"

76'-8"

COVERED   PORCH

Small, But Not Lacking

Price Code: B

■ This plan features:

— Three bedrooms

— One full and one three-quarter baths

■ Great Room adjoins the Dining Room for ease in entertaining

■ Kitchen highlighted by a peninsula counter/snack bar extending work space and offering convenience in serving informal meals or snacks

■ Split-Bedroom plan allows for privacy in the Master Bedroom with a Bath and a walk-in closet

■ Garage Entry convenient to the Kitchen

■ This home is designed with a basement foundation

MAIN FLOOR — 1,546 SQ. FT.
BASEMENT — 1,530 SQ. FT.
GARAGE — 440 SQ. FT.

TOTAL LIVING AREA:
1,546 SQ. FT.

MAIN FLOOR

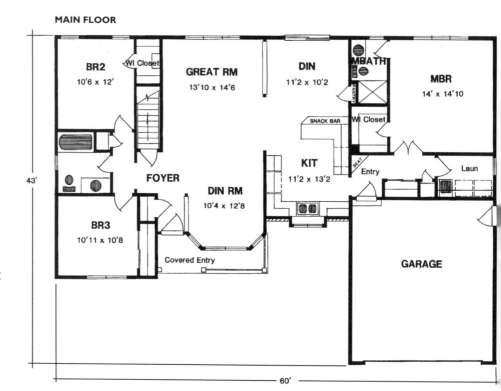

BR2
10'6 x 12'

WI Closet

GREAT RM
13'10 x 14'6

DIN
11'2 x 10'2

MBATH

MBR
14' x 14'10

SNACK BAR

WI Closet

43'

FOYER

KIT
11'2 x 13'2

Entry

Laun

BR3
10'11 x 10'8

DIN RM
10'4 x 12'8

GARAGE

Covered Entry

60'

224

To order your Blueprints, call 1-800-235-5700

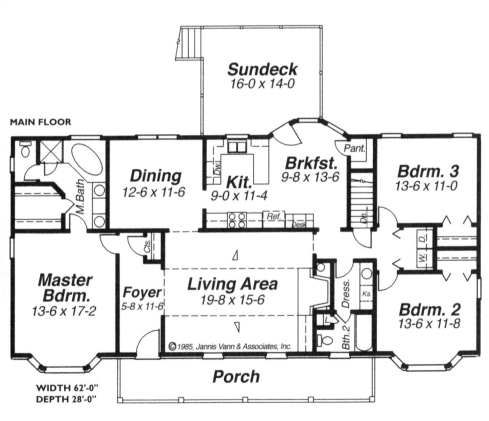

MAIN FLOOR

Sundeck
16-0 x 14-0

Dining
12-6 x 11-6

Kit.
9-0 x 11-4

Brkfst.
9-8 x 13-6

Pant.

Bdrm. 3
13-6 x 11-0

M.Bath

Ref.

Desk

W. D.

Master Bdrm.
13-6 x 17-2

Foyer
5-8 x 11-6

Living Area
19-8 x 15-6

Cts.

Dress.

Ks.

Bth.2

Bdrm. 2
13-6 x 11-8

© 1985, Jannis Vann & Associates, Inc.

Porch

WIDTH 62'-0"
DEPTH 28'-0"

Bay Windows and a Terrific Front Porch

Price Code: C

■ This plan features:

— Three bedrooms

— Two full baths

■ A Country-style front Porch

■ An expansive Living Area that includes a fireplace

■ A Master Suite with a private Master Bath and a walk-in closet

■ An efficient Kitchen serving the sunny Breakfast Area and the Dining Room with equal ease

■ A built-in Pantry and Sun Deck access add to the appeal of the Breakfast Area

■ This home is designed with a basement foundation

MAIN FLOOR — 1,778 SQ. FT.
BASEMENT — 1,008 SQ. FT.
GARAGE — 728 SQ. FT.

TOTAL LIVING AREA:
1,778 SQ. FT.

Brilliance in Brick and Fieldstone

Price Code: B

- This plan features:
  — Three bedrooms
  — Two full baths

- Hub of home is Great Room opening to Study/Formal Dining Area, covered Patio and Dining/Kitchen

- An efficient Kitchen features a Pantry, serving ledge and bright Dining Area

- Master Bedroom wing offers access to covered Patio, a huge walk-in closet and a whirlpool Bath

- This home is designed with a slab foundation

MAIN FLOOR — 1,640 SQ. FT.
GARAGE — 408 SQ. FT.

TOTAL LIVING AREA: 1,640 SQ. FT.

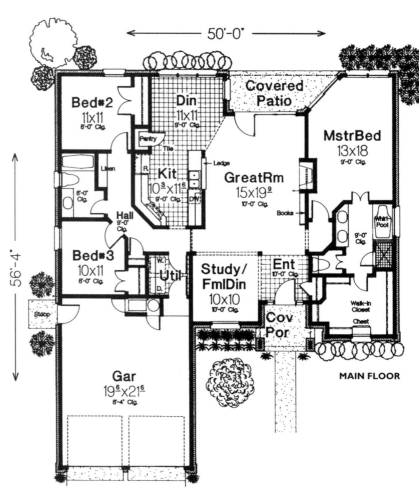

MAIN FLOOR

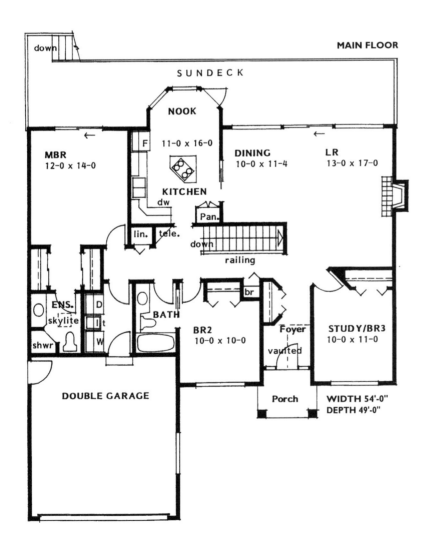

MAIN FLOOR

SUNDECK

NOOK
11-0 x 16-0

MBR
12-0 x 14-0

DINING
10-0 x 11-4

LR
13-0 x 17-0

F

KITCHEN
dw

Pan.

lin. tele.

down

railing

ENS.
skylite

D
I
t

BATH

BR2
10-0 x 10-0

br

Foyer
vaulted

STUDY/BR3
10-0 x 11-0

shwr

W

DOUBLE GARAGE

Porch

WIDTH 54'-0"
DEPTH 49'-0"

Comfort and Style

Price Code: A

■ This plan features:

— Three bedrooms

— One full and one three quarter baths

■ A walk-out basement providing additional space for family activities

■ A Master Suite complete with private Bath and skylight

■ A large Kitchen including an eating Nook

■ A Sun Deck that is easily accessible from the Master Suite, Nook and the Living/Dining Area

■ This home is designed with a basement foundation

MAIN FLOOR — 1,423 SQ. FT.
BASEMENT — 1,423 SQ. FT.
GARAGE — 399 SQ. FT.

TOTAL LIVING AREA:
1,423 SQ. FT.

For an Established Neighborhood

Price Code: A

■ This plan features:

— Three bedrooms

— Two full baths

■ A covered entrance sheltering and welcoming visitors

■ A Living Room enhanced by natural light streaming in from the large front window

■ A bayed formal Dining Room with direct access to the Sun Deck and the Living Room

■ An informal Breakfast Room with direct access to the Sun Deck

■ This home is designed with a basement foundation

MAIN FLOOR — 1,276 SQ. FT.
BASEMENT — 392 SQ. FT.
GARAGE — 728 SQ. FT.

TOTAL LIVING AREA:
1,292 SQ. FT.

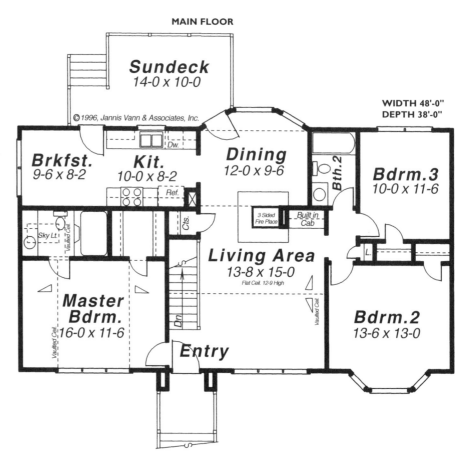

MAIN FLOOR

Sundeck
14-0 x 10-0

© 1996, Jannis Vann & Associates, Inc.

WIDTH 48'-0"
DEPTH 38'-0"

Brkfst.
9-6 x 8-2

Kit.
10-0 x 8-2

Dw.

Ref.

Dining
12-0 x 9-6

Bth. 2

Bdrm. 3
10-0 x 11-6

Sky Lt.

Vaulted Ceil.

3 Sided Fire Place

Built in Cab

Master Bdrm.
16-0 x 11-6

Vaulted Ceil.

Cts.

Dn.

Living Area
13-8 x 15-0
Flat Ceil. 12-9 High

Vaulted Ceil.

Bdrm. 2
13-6 x 13-0

Entry

To order your Blueprints, call 1-800-235-5700

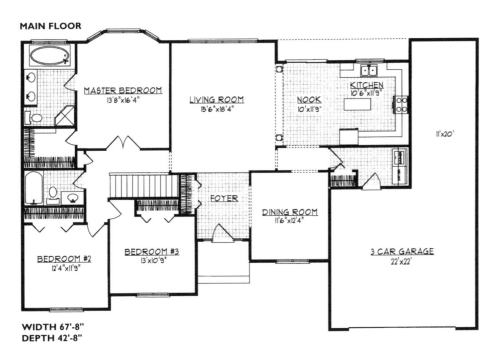

MAIN FLOOR

MASTER BEDROOM
13'8"x16'4"

LIVING ROOM
15'6"x18'4"

NOOK
10'x11'9"

KITCHEN
10'6"x11'9"

11'x20'

FOYER

DINING ROOM
11'6"x12'4"

3 CAR GARAGE
22'x22'

BEDROOM #2
12'4"x11'9"

BEDROOM #3
13'x10'9"

WIDTH 67'-8"
DEPTH 42'-8"

Triple Tandem Garage

Price Code: C

■ This plan features:

— Three bedrooms

— Two full baths

■ A large Foyer leads to the bright
and spacious Living Room

■ The open Kitchen has a central
work island

■ The Master Suite has a bay
window in the Sitting Area,
French doors and a private
Master Bath

■ A triple tandem Garage with
space for a third car, boat or just
extra space

■ This home is designed with a
basement foundation

MAIN FLOOR — 1,761 SQ. FT.
BASEMENT — 1,761 SQ. FT.
GARAGE — 658 SQ. FT.

TOTAL LIVING AREA:
1,761 SQ. FT.

WIDTH 48–10

A Stylish, Open Concept Home

Price Code: A

■ This plan features:

— Three bedrooms

— Two full baths

■ An angled Entry creates the illusion of space

■ Two columns frame the snack bar and separate the Kitchen from the Living Room

■ The Dining Area accommodates both formal and informal occasions

■ The Master Bath has a dual vanity, linen closet and whirlpool tub/shower combination

■ This home is designed with slab and crawlspace foundation options

MAIN FLOOR — 1,282 SQ. FT.

GARAGE — 501 SQ. FT.

TOTAL LIVING AREA:
1,282 SQ. FT.

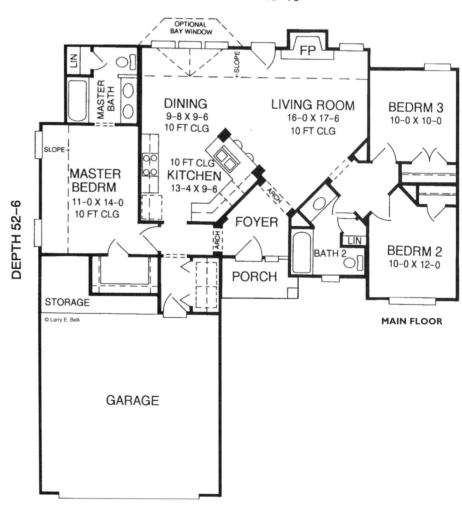

MAIN FLOOR

To order your Blueprints, call 1-800-235-5700

WIDTH 52'-0"
DEPTH 47'-0"

DECK   DN

MAIN FLOOR

BED 2
10'9 X 10'9

DW

DINING
10'0 X 11'0
VAULTED

MASTER SUITE
11'0 X 15'3

PANTRY   R & O

REF.

STORAGE   FRZ

LINEN

BED 3
10'9 X 10'9

D

LIVING
18'3 X 13'0
VAULTED

W

FAU   WH

GARAGE
21'3 X 21'9

OPTIONAL BATH

LINEN

L-Shaped Front Porch

Price Code: A

■ This plan features:

— Three bedrooms

— Two full baths

■ Attractive wood siding and a large L-shaped covered Porch

■ Generous Living Room with a vaulted ceiling

■ Large two-car Garage with access through Utility Room

■ Vaulted ceiling adds volume to the Dining Room

■ Master Suite in isolated location enhanced by abundant closet space, separate vanity and linen storage

■ This home is designed with a crawlspace foundation

MAIN FLOOR — 1,280 SQ. FT.

TOTAL LIVING AREA:
1,280 SQ. FT.

PLAN NO. 63141

WIDTH 58'-2"
DEPTH 59'-10"

Bedroom 2
10' · 11'

Bedroom 3
12' · 11'

Bath

fireplace

Utility

Patio

Brkfst
Nook

Family Room
18' · 11'
volume ceiling

Bedroom 4
12' · 11'

Master Suite
15' · 11'
volume ceiling

Dining
13'-9"

Kitchen

volume ceiling

ac   wh

w.i.c.

Living Room
15' · 11'

Foyer

Double Garage

Bath

MAIN FLOOR

Making the Most of Living Spaces

Price Code: C

■ This plan features:
— Four bedrooms
— Two full baths
■ The L-shaped Living/Dining Areas create a private nook for quiet entertaining
■ The Kitchen is surrounded by Breakfast Area and Family Room
■ The secluded Master Suite comes with a soaking tub and private toilet/shower space for efficiency
■ Perfect for growing families, the secondary Bedrooms are grouped around Bath and Laundry
■ A traditional, formal elevation adds stature to the home's street appeal
■ This home is designed with a slab foundation

MAIN FLOOR — 1,906 SQ. FT.
GARAGE — 444 SQ. FT.

TOTAL LIVING AREA:
1,906 SQ. FT.

PLAN NO. 69014

What A Backyard View!

Price Code: B

■ This plan features:
— Three bedrooms
— Two full baths
■ This magnificent home includes a wall of windows in the back and two covered Porches
■ A three-car Garage provides all the storage you need for the tools to maintain your estate
■ Enjoy family meals in the vaulted-ceiling Dining Room
■ Efficiency and style mark the Kitchen and Breakfast Area
■ This home is designed with basement, slab, and crawlspace foundation options

MAIN FLOOR — 1,721 SQ. FT

TOTAL LIVING AREA:
1,906 SQ. FT.

83'-0"

42'-0"

Atrium Below   **MAIN FLOOR**
Dn

Covered
Porch

Brk
11-5x12-0

Great Rm
16-0x16-10
vaulted

MBr
16-0x14-0
vaulted

Kit
11-5x
12-0

Garage
29-4x21-4

Dining
11-0x11-6

Br 3
11-1x13-3

Br 2
11-0x12-9

Porch
27-8x5-0

To order your Blueprints, call 1-800-235-5700

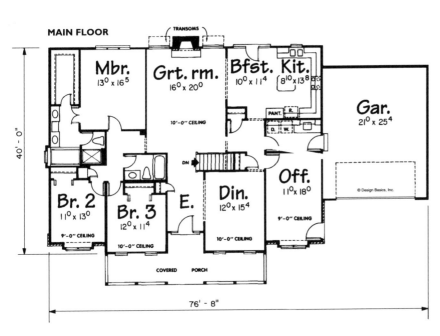

MAIN FLOOR

TRANSOMS

Mbr.
13⁰ x 16⁵

Grt. rm.
16⁰ x 20⁰

Bfst.
10⁰ x 11⁴

Kit.
8¹⁰x13⁸

10'-0" CEILING

PANT.

R.

Gar.
21⁰ x 25⁴

D. W.

Br. 2
11⁰ x 13⁰

9'-0" CEILING

Br. 3
12⁰ x 11⁴

10'-0" CEILING

E.

DN

Din.
12⁰ x 15⁴

10'-0" CEILING

Off.
11⁰ x 18⁰

9'-0" CEILING

© Design Basics, Inc.

COVERED PORCH

40' - 0"

76' - 8"

Work Comfortably in Your Home Office

Price Code: D

■ This plan features:

— Three bedrooms

— Two full baths

■ The Entry leads directly into the formal Dining Room or the Great Room, and is ideal for guest traffic

■ The Office has its own private entrance and bump-out window

■ Counter space is abundant in the U-shaped Kitchen and adds convenience and practicality to preparing meals

■ The Master Suite features a roomy walk-in closet and luxurious Bath

■ This home is designed with a basement foundation

■ Alternate foundation options available at an additional charge. Please call 1-800-235-5700 for more information.

MAIN FLOOR — 2,151 SQ. FT.

TOTAL LIVING AREA:
2,151 SQ. FT.

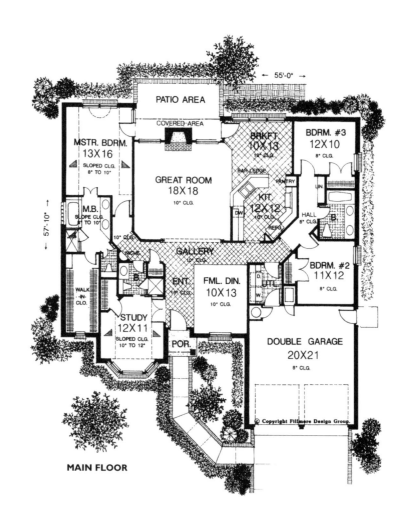

Packed with Options

Price Code: D

- This plan features:
— Three bedrooms
— Two full and one half baths

- The Great Room has a rear wall fireplace that is set between windows

- Both Dining Areas are located steps away from the Kitchen

- The Study has a sloped ceiling and a front bay of windows

- The Master Bedroom has a private Bath and a galley-like walk-in closet

- This home is designed with a slab foundation

MAIN FLOOR — 2,081 SQ. FT.
GARAGE — 422 SQ. FT.

TOTAL LIVING AREA: 2,081 SQ. FT.

MAIN FLOOR

PATIO AREA
COVERED AREA
MSTR. BDRM. 13X16
SLOPED CLG. 8' TO 10'
M.B.
SLOPE CLG. TO 10'
GREAT ROOM 18X18
10' CLG.
BRKFT 10X13
BDRM. #3 12X10
8' CLG.
BAR-LEDGE
PANTRY
KIT. 12X12
DW
REFG.
HALL 8' CLG.
B
GALLERY 8' CLG.
WALK-IN-CLO.
B
ENT.
FML. DIN. 10X13
10' CLG.
D
UTIL
W
BDRM. #2 11X12
8' CLG.
STUDY 12X11
SLOPED CLG. 10' TO 12'
POR.
DOUBLE GARAGE 20X21
8' CLG.
← 55'-0" →
57'-10"
© Copyright Fillmore Design Group.

234

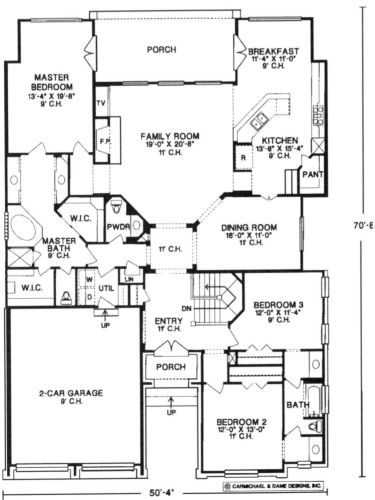

PORCH

BREAKFAST
11'-4" X 11'-0"
9' C.H.

MASTER
BEDROOM
13'-4" X 19'-8"
9' C.H.

TV

FAMILY ROOM
19'-0" X 20'-8"
11' C.H.

KITCHEN
13'-8" X 15'-4"
9' C.H.

F.P.

PANT

R

W.I.C.

PWDR

MASTER
BATH
9' C.H.

DINING ROOM
16'-0" X 11'-0"
11' C.H.

11' C.H.

70'-8

W.I.C.

W
D

UTIL

LIN

DN

BEDROOM 3
12'-0" X 11'-4"
9' C.H.

UP

ENTRY
11' C.H.

PORCH

2-CAR GARAGE
9' C.H.

UP

BEDROOM 2
12'-0" X 13'-0"
11' C.H.

BATH

© CARMICHAEL & DAME DESIGNS, INC.

50'-4"

MAIN FLOOR

Classic Brick Exterior

Price Code: E

■ This plan features:

— Three bedrooms

— Two full and one half baths

■ An 11-foot ceiling adorning the Foyer

■ Private access to the full Bath from the secondary Bedrooms

■ Central Family Room accented by a fireplace and a built-in entertainment center

■ Secluded Master Suite highlighted by a lavish Master Bath

■ This home is designed with a slab foundation

■ Alternate foundation options available at an additional charge. Please call 1-800-235-5700 for more information.

MAIN FLOOR — 2,404 SQ. FT.
GARAGE — 493 SQ. FT.

TOTAL LIVING AREA:
2,404 SQ. FT.

Rear Elevation

Beautiful and Functional

Price Code: D

■ This plan features:

— Three bedrooms

— Two full and one helf baths

■ Gracious, keystone arch Entry opens to formal Dining Room and Great Room beyond

■ Spacious Great Room features fireplace surrounded by windows topped by a cathedral ceiling

■ Kitchen/Nook layout ideal for busy household with easy access to Deck, Dining Room, Laundry and Garage

■ This home is designed with a slab foundation

MAIN FLOOR — 2,404 SQ. FT.
GARAGE — 493 SQ. FT.

TOTAL LIVING AREA:
2,404 SQ. FT.

MAIN FLOOR

WD. DECK
12'0" X 12'0"

BR. #2
12'0" X 11'8"

GRT. RM.
CATHEDRAL CLG.
16'0" X 20'0"

NK.
10'6" X 12'0"

KIT.
10'6" X 12'0"

MBR.
16'0" X 13'0"

PAN.

DN.

BR. #3
12'0" X 11'0"

E.
11' 1-1/8"
CEILING HGT.

DIN.
TRAY CEILING
12'0" X 13'0"

3 CAR GAR.
34'0" X 22'0"

WIDTH 50'-4"
DEPTH 70'-8"

To order your Blueprints, call 1-800-235-5700

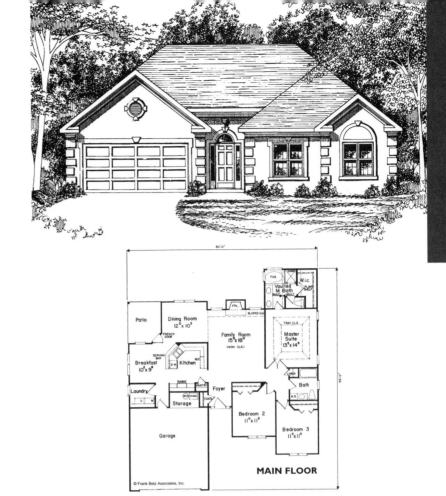

Features of a Larger Home

Price Code: B

- This plan features:
  — Three bedrooms
  — Two full baths
- The Master Suite is topped in a tray ceiling and includes a walk-in closet and a vaulted ceiling over the Master Bath
- The Kitchen flows easily into the Breakfast Area and the formal Dining Room is just a few short steps away
- A French door leads to the Patio Area, expanding living space to the outdoors
- The Family Room is at the heart of the home and is open to the Dining Room for ease in entertaining and is enhanced by a high ceiling and a fireplace
- This home is designed with slab and crawlspace foundation options

MAIN FLOOR — 1,531 SQ. FT.
BASEMENT — 1,527 SQ. FT.
GARAGE — 441 SQ. FT.

TOTAL LIVING AREA:
1,531 SQ. FT.

PLAN NO. 98496

MAIN FLOOR

© Frank Betz Associates, Inc.

Open Spaces

Price Code: A

- This plan features:
  — Three bedrooms
  — Two full baths
- An open layout between the Living Room, Dining Room and Kitchen creating and illusion of spaciousness
- A peninsula counter/eating bar for a quick meal separating the Kitchen from the Living Room
- A vaulted ceiling in the Living Room adding volume to the room
- A Laundry center located near the Bedrooms for efficiency
- This home is designed with a slab foudation

MAIN FLOOR — 1,120 SQ. FT.
GARAGE — 288 SQ. FT.

TOTAL LIVING AREA:
1,120 SQ. FT.

PLAN NO. 96538

MAIN FLOOR

To order your Blueprints, call 1-800-235-5700

Single-Level Three Bedroom

Price Code: A

- This plan features:
  — Three bedrooms
  — Two full baths
- A great first impression is received from the moment you step into the Foyer which is topped by a vaulted ceiling
- The Family Room has a corner fireplace and is also topped by a vaulted ceiling
- The Kitchen flows into the Breakfast Room and features a convenient pass-thru to the Family Room
- A convenient Laundry Center is located in the Breakfast Room
- The Master Suite includes a tray ceiling over the Bedroom and a vaulted ceiling over the Bath
- This home is designed with basement, slab, and crawlspace foundation options

MAIN FLOOR — 1,169 SQ. FT.
BASEMENT — 1,194 SQ. FT.
GARAGE — 400 SQ. FT.

TOTAL LIVING AREA: 1,169 SQ. FT.

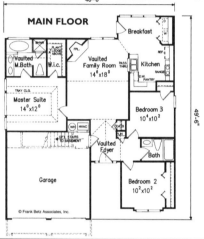

Outdoor Space

Price Code: C

- This plan features:
  — Three bedrooms
  — Two full and one half baths
- Floors in the high traffic areas—Foyer, Bathrooms, Kitchen, and Utility Room—are tiled to ease clean up
- A covered Porch, Greenhouse, and fenced-in Garden make this home a nature lover's dream
- The centralized Kitchen has easy access to the formal Dining Room, Breakfast Nook, and generous Family Room
- The Master Suite features a spacious walk-in closet with built-ins and a luxurious Bath, with a tub that overlooks the garden
- This home is designed with a basement foundation

MAIN FLOOR — 1,997 SQ. FT.
GARAGE — 502 SQ. FT.
BONUS — 310 SQ. FT.

TOTAL LIVING AREA: 1,997 SQ. FT.

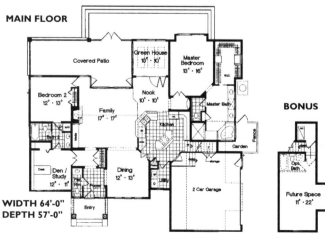

To order your Blueprints, call 1-800-235-5700

Cozy Front Porch

Price Code: A

This plan features:

Three bedrooms

Two full baths

Terrific Great Room with 12-foot ceiling and fireplace flanked by windows

Kitchen/Breakfast Room with ample counter space and storage

Laundry Room doubles as a Mudroom

The Master Bedroom includes a private, double vanity Bath and a walk-in closet

The two additional Bedrooms are in close proximity to the full Bath in the hall

This home is designed with a basement foundation

MAIN FLOOR — 1,433 SQ. FT.

GARAGE — 504 SQ. FT.

TOTAL LIVING AREA:
1,433 SQ. FT.

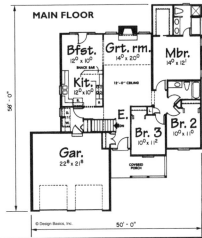

Four Bedroom

Price Code: B

This plan features:

– Four bedrooms

– Two full baths

A vaulted ceiling of the Foyer with convenient coat closet

A vaulted ceiling crowning the Family Room with a French door to the rear yard and a cozy fireplace

Efficient Kitchen located between the formal and informal dining areas for ease in serving

Tray ceiling topping the Master Bedroom and a vaulted ceiling crowning the Master Bath

Secondary Bedrooms located near the full Bath in the hall with a window seat accenting one Bedroom and a vaulted ceiling highlighting another

This home is designed with basement, slab, and crawlspace foundation options

MAIN FLOOR — 1,688 SQ. FT.

BASEMENT — 1,702 SQ. FT.

GARAGE — 402 SQ. FT.

TOTAL LIVING AREA:
1,688 SQ. FT.

PLAN NO. 97494

Beautiful Lines

Price Code: D

■ This plan features:

— Three bedrooms

— Two full and one half baths

■ This uniqely L-shaped Kitchen includes a wetbar and has direct access to the Breakfast Nook, Dining Room, and Great Room

■ Garage plan includes built-in workbench for hobbies and repairs

■ The spacious Master Suite has a walk-in closet and large Master Bath with all the amenities

■ This home is designed with a basement foundation

■ Alternate foundation options available at an additional charge. Please call 1-800-235-5700 for more information.

MAIN FLOOR — 2,186 SQ. FT.
GARAGE — 720 SQ. FT.

TOTAL LIVING AREA:
2,186 SQ. FT.

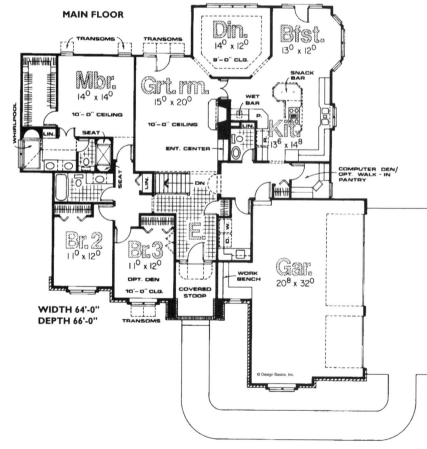

MAIN FLOOR

WIDTH 64'-0"
DEPTH 66'-0"

© Design Basics, Inc.

240

To order your Blueprints, call 1-800-235-5700

Attention to Detail

Price Code: C

■ This plan features:
— Three bedrooms
— Two full and one half baths

■ A 12-foot ceiling, large window and decorative columns highlight the elegant Dining Room

■ Vaulted ceiling tops the Family Room, which is further accented by a fireplace

■ This home is designed with basement and crawlspace foundation options

MAIN FLOOR — 1,861 SQ. FT.
GARAGE — 450 SQ. FT.
BASEMENT — 1,898 SQ. FT.

TOTAL LIVING AREA:
1,861 SQ. FT.

WIDTH 58'-6"
DEPTH 56'-0"

Breakfast

FRENCH DOOR

FPL.

VLT.

SERVING BAR

Vaulted Family Room
17⁵ x 20⁰
12'-0" HIGH CLG.

TRAY CLG.

Master Suite
13⁵ x 17⁴

SHWR.

Vaulted M.Bath

LINEN

PLANT SHELF ABOVE

W.i.c.

PANTRY

RANGE

DW

Kitchen

DECORATIVE COLUMNS

PLANT SHELF ABOVE

Foyer
12'-0" HIGH CEILING

Pwdr.

W.i.c.

Bedroom 2
11⁰ x 11⁰

REF.

Dining Room
12⁰ x 12²
12'-0" HIGH CLG.

COATS

LINEN

Bath

Laund.

D. W.

COVERED ENTRY

Bedroom 3
12⁸ x 11³

copyright © 1998 frank betz associates, inc.

Garage
19⁵ x 20³

GARAGE LOCATION WITH BASEMENT

MAIN FLOOR

Laund.
D. W.

Dining Room
12⁰ x 12²
12'-0" HIGH CLG.

COATS

STAIRS DN.

Stor.

Garage
19⁵ x 20⁴

OPTIONAL BASEMENT STAIR LOCATION

Eye-Catching Dining Room

Price Code: A

- This plan features:
  — Three bedrooms
  — Two full baths
- Two-story window allows for streaming sunlight to enter the Dining Room
- Crowning vaulted ceiling over the Great Room
- Tray ceiling highlighting the Master Bedroom and a vaulted ceiling over the Master Bath
- French door from the Breakfast Room leading to the rear yard
- Laundry Center located at the end of the Breakfast Room
- This home is designed with basement and crawl-space foundation options

MAIN FLOOR — 1,271 SQ. FT.
GARAGE — 400 SQ. FT.
BASEMENT — 1,292 SQ. FT.

TOTAL LIVING AREA:
1,271 SQ. FT.

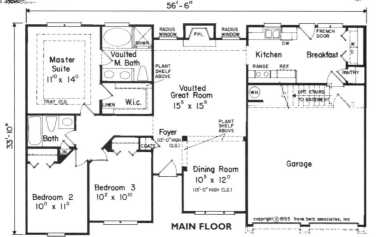

56'-6"

33'-10"

Master Suite 11¹⁰ x 14⁰

TRAY CLG.

Vaulted M. Bath

SHWR.

PLANT SHELF ABOVE

LINEN   W.i.c.

Bath

LIN

Bedroom 2 10⁰ x 11⁰

Bedroom 3 10² x 10¹⁰

COATS

Foyer (13'-0" HIGH CLG.)

Dining Room 10³ x 12⁰ (13'-0" HIGH CLG.)

RADIUS WINDOW   FPL.   RADIUS WINDOW

Vaulted Great Room 15⁶ x 15⁶

PLANT SHELF ABOVE

W.H.

OPT. STAIRS TO BASEMENT

DW

Kitchen   **Breakfast**

RANGE   REF.

PNTRY

FRENCH DOOR

W. D.

Garage

copyright © 1993 frank betz associates, inc.

MAIN FLOOR

WIDTH 80-6

Dignified Traditional

Price Code: E

- This plan features:
  — Four bedrooms
  — Two full and one half baths
- Dramatic columns defining the elegant Dining Room and framing the entrance to the large, spacious Great Room
- A Breakfast Bar and work island in the gourmet Kitchen which also includes an abundance of counter and cabinet space
- All Bedrooms conveniently grouped at the opposite side of the home
- A Master Suite with an enormous walk-in closet and a luxuriant Master Bath
- Bedrooms two and three also have walk-in closets and share a full Bath with a double vanity
- This home is designed with crawlspace and slab foundation options

MAIN FLOOR — 2,292 SQ. FT.
GARAGE — 526 SQ. FT.

TOTAL LIVING AREA:
2,292 SQ. FT.

DEPTH 50-6

MSTR BATH

MASTER BEDROOM 14-0 X 15-0 10 FT CLG

BEDROOM 4 /STUDY 11-4 X 10-0 8 FT CLG

FP

GREAT ROOM 16-10 X 16-10 12 FT CLG

+10 FT CLG LINE

BRKFST RM 12-6 X 10-6 10 FT CLG

MAIN FLOOR

UTILITY 11-8 X 6-6

PWDR

BATH 2

FOYER 10 FT CLG

ARCH

KITCHEN 12-6 X 16-10

42" LEDGE

DINING ROOM 14-8 X 13-4 12 FT CLG

10 FT CLG

GARAGE

© Larry E. Belk

BEDROOM 2 11-2 X 12-2 8 FT CLG

BEDROOM 3 12-4 X 11-8 8 FT CLG

PORCH

STORAGE

Decorative Ceiling Treatments

Price Code: C

■ This plan features:
— Three bedrooms
— Two full baths
■ Covered front Porch creating curb appeal and extending living space
■ A tray ceiling crowning the Great Room which includes a corner fireplace and access to the rear Deck
■ Dining Area open to the Kitchen with angled snack bar for meals on the go
■ Split Bedroom floor plan assuring the Master Suite of privacy
■ A tray ceiling topping the Master Bedroom which has direct access to a whirlpool Master Bath
■ This home is designed with a crawlspace foundation

MAIN FLOOR — 1,765 SQ. FT.
GARAGE — 440 SQ. FT.

TOTAL LIVING AREA:
1,765 SQ. FT.

MAIN FLOOR

Eye-Catching Elevation

Price Code: D

■ This plan features:
— Four bedrooms
— Two full baths
■ Expansive Great Room with a vaulted ceiling and a fireplace with windows to either side
■ Arched openings accented by columns accessing the formal Dining Room
■ Efficient Kitchen with built-in Pantry, serving bar and double sinks
■ Tray ceiling topping the Master Bedroom and a vaulted ceiling over the luxurious Master Bath
■ Super walk-in closet in Master Suite with a plant shelf
■ This home is designed with a basement foundation

MAIN FLOOR — 2,032 SQ. FT.
BASEMENT — 1,471 SQ. FT.
GARAGE — 561 SQ. FT.

TOTAL LIVING AREA:
2,032 SQ. FT.

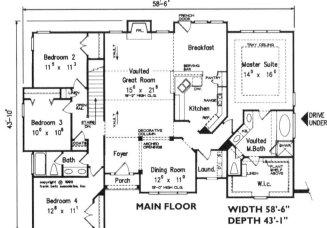

MAIN FLOOR

WIDTH 58'-6"
DEPTH 43'-1"

Stone and Siding

Price Code: B

■ This plan features:

— Three bedrooms

— Two full baths

■ Ample cabinet and counter space with a built-in Pantry and serving bar in the Kitchen

■ French door to the outdoors or an optional bay window in the Breakfast Room

■ A vaulted ceiling crowning the Great Room, highlighted by a fireplace

■ Master Suite has a tray ceiling and a plush Master Bath

■ This home is designed with a basement foundation

MAIN FLOOR — 1,571 SQ. FT.
BONUS — 334 SQ. FT.
BASEMENT — 1,642 SQ. FT.
GARAGE — 483 SQ. FT.

TOTAL LIVING AREA:
1,517 SQ. FT.

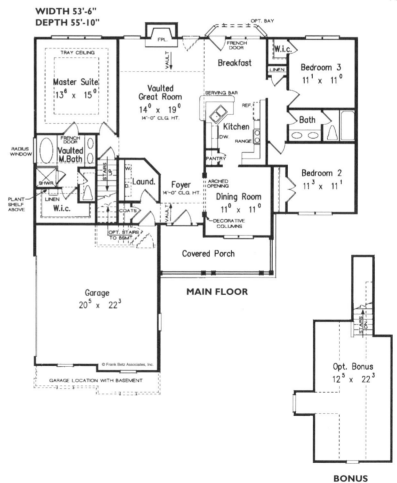

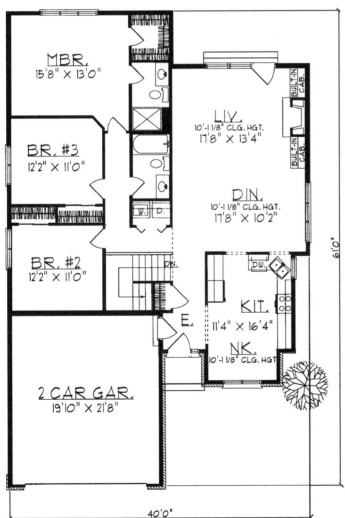

MAIN FLOOR

Cute Starter Home

Price Code: B

■ This plan features:

— Three bedrooms

— Two full baths

■ Spacious Living/Dining Room allows comfortable gatherings with multiple windows and outdoor access

■ Open Kitchen/Nook easily accesses Dining Area, Laundry closet and Garage

■ Corner Master Bedroom boasts full view of rear yard, walk-in closet and private Bath

■ This home is designed with a basement foundation

MAIN FLOOR — 1,557 SQ. FT.
BASEMENT — 1,557 SQ. FT.
GARAGE — 400 SQ. FT.

TOTAL LIVING AREA:
1,557 SQ. FT.

Outstanding Arched Window

Price Code: E

- This plan features:
  — Three bedrooms
  — Two full and one half baths

- Expansive Family Room accented by a fireplace and active dormer with radius window

- Luxurious Master Suite highlighted by a tray ceiling, private Sitting Room and Master Bath

- Efficient Kitchen including double oven and work island

- This home is designed with basement, slab, and crawlspace foundation options

MAIN FLOOR — 2,322 SQ. FT.
BASEMENT — 2,322 SQ. FT.
GARAGE — 453 SQ. FT.

TOTAL LIVING AREA:
2,322 SQ. FT.

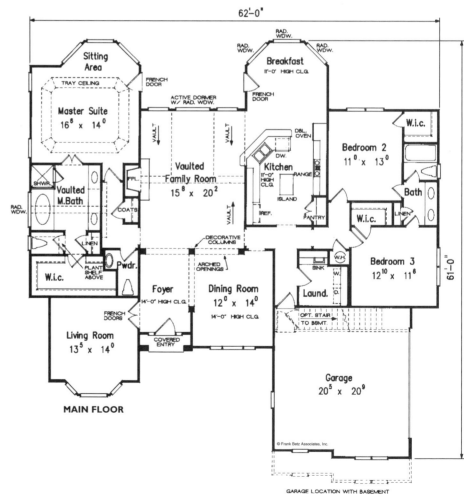

Exterior Elevations

Scaled drawings of the front, rear, sides of the home. Information pertaining to the exterior finish materials, roof pitches and exterior height dimensions.

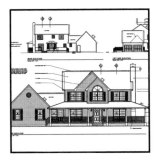

Cabinet Plans

These plans, or in some cases elevations, will detail the lay-out of the kitchen and bath-room cabinets at a larger scale. Available for most plans.

Typical Wall Section

This section will address insulation, roof components and interior and exterior wall finishes. Your plans will be designed with either 2x4 or 2x6 exterior walls, but most professional contractors can easily adapt the plans to the wall thickness you require.

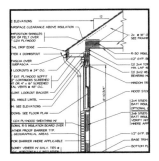

Fireplace Details

If the home you have chosen includes a fireplace, the fire-place detail will show typical methods to construct the fire-box, hearth and flue chase for masonry units, or a wood frame chase for a zero-clear-ance unit. Available for most plans.

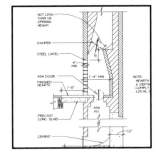

Foundation Plan

These plans will accurately dimension the footprint of your home including load bearing points and beam placement if applicable. The foundation style will vary from plan to plan.

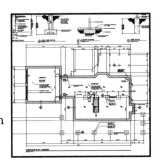

Roof Plan

The information necessary to construct the roof will be included with your home plans. Some plans will refer-ence roof trusses, while many others contain schematic framing plans. These framing plans will indicate the lumber sizes necessary for the rafters and ridgeboards based on the designated roof loads.

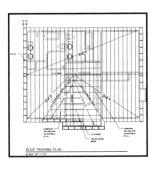

Typical Cross-Section

A cut-away cross-section through the entire home shows your building contractor the exact correlation of con-struction components at all levels of the house. It will help to clarify the load bearing points from the roof all the way down to the basement. Available for most plans.

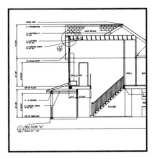

Detailed Floor Plans

The floor plans of your home accurately dimension the posi-tioning of all walls, doors, windows, stairs and permanent fixtures. They will show you the relationship and dimen-sions of rooms, closets and traffic patterns. The schematic of the electrical layout may be included in the plan.

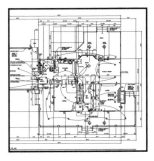

Stair Details

If stairs are an element of the design you have chosen, the plans will show the necessary information to build these, either through a stair cross-section or on the floor plans.

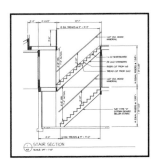

Garlinghouse Options & Extras

Reversed Plans Can Make Your Dream Home Just Right!

You could have exactly the home you want by flipping it end-for-end. Simply order your plans "reversed." We'll send you one full set of mirror-image plans (with the writing backwards) as a master guide for you and your builder.

The remaining sets of your order will come as shown in this book so the dimensions and specifications are easily read on the job site...but most plans in our collection come stamped "reversed" so there is no confusion.

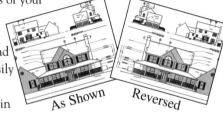

As Shown   Reversed

We can only send reversed plans with multiple-set orders. There is a $50 charge for this service.

Some plans in our collection are available in Right Reading Reverse. Right Reading Reverse plans will show your home in reverse, with the writing on the plan being readable. This easy-to-read format will save you valuable time and money. Please contact our Customer Service Department to check for Right Reading Reverse availability. There is a $135 charge for Right Reading Reverse. **RRR**

Remember To Order Your Materials List

Available at a modest additional charge, the Materials List gives the quantity, dimensions, and specifications for the major materials needed to build your home. You will get faster, more accurate bids from your contractors and building suppliers — and avoid paying for unused materials and waste. Materials Lists are available for all home plans except as otherwise indicated, but can only be ordered with a set of home plans. Due to differences in regional requirements and homeowner or builder preferences... electrical, plumbing and heating/air conditioning equipment specifications are not designed specifically for each plan. **ML**

What Garlinghouse Offers

Home Plan Blueprint Package

By purchasing a multiple set package of blueprints or a vellum from Garlinghouse, you not only receive the physical blueprint documents necessary for construction, but you are also granted a license to build one, and only one, home. You can also make simple modifications, including minor non-structural changes and material substitutions to our design, as long as these changes are made directly on the blueprints purchased from Garlinghouse and no additional copies are made.

Home Plan Vellums

By purchasing vellums for one of our home plans, you receive the same construction drawings found in the blueprints, but printed on vellum paper. Vellums can be erased and are perfect for making design changes. They are also semi-transparent making them easy to duplicate. But most importantly, the purchase of home plan vellums comes with a broader license that allows you to make changes to the design (ie, create a hand drawn or CAD derivative work), to make copies of the plan and to build one home from the plan.

License To Build Additional Homes

With the purchase of a blueprint package or vellums you automatically receive a license to build one home and only one home, respectively. If you want to build more homes than you are licensed to build through your purchase of a plan, then additional licenses may be purchased at reasonable costs from Garlinghouse. Inquire for more information.

Modify Your Favorite Design, Made Easy

#1 Modifying Your Garlinghouse Home Plan

Simple modifications to your dream home, including minor non-structural changes and material substitutions, can be made between you and your builder by marking the changes directly on your blueprints. However, if you are considering making significant changes to your chosen design, we recommend that you use the services of The Garlinghouse Design Staff. We will help take your ideas and turn them into a reality, just the way you want. Here's our procedure!

When you place your Vellum order, you may also request a free Garlinghouse Modification Kit. In this kit, you will receive a red marking pencil, furniture cut-out sheet, ruler, a self addressed mailing label and a form for specifying any additional notes or drawings that will help us understand your design ideas. Mark your desired changes directly on the Vellum drawings. NOTE: Please use only a **red pencil** to mark your desired changes on the Vellum. Then, return the redlined Vellum set in the original box to us.

Important: Please roll the Vellums for shipping, *do not fold*.

We also offer modification estimates. We will provide you with an estimate to draft your changes based on your specific modifications before you purchase the vellums, for a $50 fee. After you receive your estimate, if you decide to have us do the changes, the $50 estimate fee will be deducted from the cost of your modifications. If, however, you choose to use a different service, the $50 estimate fee is non-refundable. (Note: Personal checks cannot be accepted for the estimate.)

Within 5 days of receipt of your plans, you will be contacted by a member of the design staff with an estimate for the design services to draw those changes. A 50% deposit is required before we begin making the actual modifications to your plans.

Once the design changes have been completed to your vellum plan, a representative will call to inform you that your modified Vellum plan is complete and will be shipped as soon as the final payment has been made. For additional information call us at 1-860-659-5667. Please refer to the Modification Pricing Guide for estimated modification costs.

#2 Reproducible Vellums for Local Modification Ease

If you decide not to use Garlinghouse for your modifications, we recommend that you follow our same procedure of purchasing Vellums. You then have the option of using the services of the original designer of the plan, a local professional designer, or architect to make the modifications.

With a Vellum copy of our plans, a design professional can alter the drawings just the way you want, then you can print as many copies of the modified plans as you need to build your house. And, since you have already started with our complete detailed plans, the cost of those expensive professional services will be significantly less than starting from scratch. Refer to the price schedule for Vellum costs.

MODIFICATION PRICING GUIDE

CATEGORIES	ESTIMATED COST
Kitchen Layout Plan and Elevation	$175.00
Bathroom Layout Plan and Elevation	$175.00
Fireplace Plan and Details	$200.00
Interior Elevation	$125.00
Exterior Elevation Material Change	$140.00
Exterior Elevation Add Brick or Stone	$400.00
Exterior Elevation Style Change	$450.00
Non Bearing Walls(interior)	$200.00
Bearing and/or Exterior Walls	$325.00
Wall Framing Change 2x4 to 2x6 or 2x6 to 2x4	$240.00
Add/Reduce Living Space Square Footage	Quote Required
New Materials List	Quote Required
Change Trusses to Rafters or Change Roof Pitch	$300.00
Framing Plan Changes	$325.00
Garage Changes	$325.00
Add a Foundation Option	$300.00
Foundation Changes	$250.00
Right Reading Plan Reverse	$575.00
Architects Seal (available for most states)	$300.00
Energy Certificate	$150.00
Light and Ventilation Schedule	$150.00

Questions?

Call our customer service department at **1.860.659.5667**

Ignoring Copyright Laws Can Be
A $100,000 Mistake

Recent changes in the US Copyright Laws allow for statutory penalties of up to $100,000 per incident for copyright infringement involving any of the copyrighted plans found in this publication. The law can be confusing. So, for your own protection, take the time to understand what you can and cannot do when it comes to home plans.

What You Can't Do!

You Cannot Duplicate Home Plans
Purchasing a set of blueprints and making additional sets by reproducing the original is illegal. If you need multiple sets of a particular home plan, you must purchase them.

You Cannot Copy Any Part of a Home Plan to Create Another
Creating your own plan by copying even part of a home design found in this publication is called "creating a derivative work" and is illegal unless you have permission to do so.

You Cannot Build a Home Without a License
You must have specific permission or license to build a home from a copyrighted design, even if the finished home has been changed from the original plan. It is illegal to build one of the homes found in this publication without a license.

"How to obtain a construction cost calculation based on labor rates and building material costs in your Zip Code area!"

Why? Do you wish you could quickly find out the building cost for your new home without waiting for a contractor to compile hundreds of bids? Would you like to have a benchmark to compare your contractor(s) bids against? Well, Now You Can!, with Zip-Quote Home Cost Calculator. Zip-Quote is only available for zip code areas within the United States.

How? Our Zip-Quote Home Cost Calculator will enable you to obtain the calculated building cost to construct your new home, based on labor rates and building material costs within your zip code area without the normal delays or hassles usually associated with the bidding process. Zip-Quote can be purchased in two separate formats, an itemized or a bottom line format.

"How does Zip-Quote actually work?" When you call to order, you must choose from the options available for your specific home, in order for us to process your order. Once we receive your Zip-Quote order, we process your specific home plan building materials list through our Home Cost Calculator which contains up-to-date rates for all residential labor trades and building material costs in your zip code area. "The result?" A calculated cost to build your dream home in your zip code area. This calculation will help you (as a consumer or a builder) evaluate your building budget.

All database information for our calculations is furnished by Marshall & Swift L.P. For over 60 years, Marshall & Swift L.P. has been a leading provider of cost data to professionals in all aspects of the construction and remodeling industries.

Option 1- The **Itemized Zip-Quote** is a detailed building material list. Each building material list line item will separately state the labor cost, material cost and equipment cost (if applicable) for the use of that building material in the construction process. This building materials list will be summarized by the individual building categories and will have additional columns where you can enter data from your contractor's estimates for a cost comparison between the different suppliers and contractors who will actually quote you their products and services.

Option 2- The **Bottom Line Zip-Quote** is a one line summarized total cost for the home plan of your choice. This cost calculation is also based on the labor cost, material cost and equipment cost (if applicable) within your local zip code area. Bottom Line Zip-Quote is available for most plans. Please call for availability.

Cost The price of your Itemized Zip-Quote is based upon the pricing schedule of the plan you have selected, in addition to the price of the materials list. Please refer to the pricing schedule on our order form. The price of your initial Bottom Line Zip-Quote is $29.95. Each additional Bottom Line Zip-Quote ordered in conjunction with the initial order is only $14.95. Bottom Line Zip-Quote may be purchased separately and does NOT have to be purchased in conjunction with a home plan order.

FYI An Itemized Zip-Quote Home Cost Calculation can ONLY be purchased in conjunction with a Home Plan order. The Itemized Zip-Quote can not be purchased separately. If you find within 60 days of your order date that you will be unable to build this home, you may then exchange the plans and the materials list towards the price of a new set of plans (see order info pages for plan exchange policy). The Itemized Zip-Quote and the Bottom Line Zip-Quote are NOT returnable. The price of the initial Bottom Line Zip-Quote order can be credited towards the purchase of an Itemized Zip-Quote order, only if available. Additional Bottom Line Zip-Quote orders, within the same order can not be credited. Please call our Customer Service Department for more information. **ZIP**

An Itemized Zip-Quote is available for plans where you see this symbol. **BL**

A Bottom-line Zip-Quote is available for all plans under 4,000 sq. ft. or where you see this symbol.

Please call for current availability.

Some More Information The Itemized and Bottom Line Zip-Quotes give you approximated costs for constructing the particular house in your area. These costs are not exact and are only intended to be used as a preliminary estimate to help determine the affordability of a new home and/or as a guide to evaluate the general competitiveness of actual price quotes obtained through local suppliers and contractors. However, Zip-Quote cost figures should never be relied upon as the only source of information in either case. **Land, landscaping, sewer systems, site work, contractor overhead and profit and other expenses are not included in our building cost figures. Excluding land and landscaping, you may incur an additional 20% to 40% in costs from the original estimate.** Garlinghouse and Marshall & Swift L.P. can not guarantee any level of data accuracy or correctness in a Zip-Quote and disclaim all liability for loss with respect to the same, in excess of the original purchase price of the Zip-Quote product. All Zip-Quote calculations are based upon the actual blueprints and do not reflect any differences or options that may be shown on the published house renderings, floor plans or photographs.

the Garlinghouse company

BEST PLAN VALUE IN THE INDUSTRY!

Order Code No. **H2SL9**

Order Form

Plan prices guaranteed until 5/1/03 After this date call for updated pricing

_____ foundation

____ set(s) of blueprints for plan #_____ $_____

____ Vellum & Modification kit for plan #_____ $_____

____ Additional set(s) @ $50 each for plan #_____ $_____

____ Mirror Image Reverse @ $50 each $_____

____ Right Reading Reverse @ $135 each $_____

____ Materials list for plan #_____ $_____

____ Detail Plans @ $19.95 each

     ❏ Construction ❏ Plumbing ❏ Electrical $_____

____ Bottom line ZIP Quote@$29.95 for plan #_____ $_____

____ Additional Bottom Line Zip Quote

     @ $14.95 for plan(s) #_____ $_____

   Zip Code where building _____

____ Itemized ZIP Quote for plan(s) #_____ $_____

   Shipping $_____

   Subtotal $_____

   Sales Tax *(CT residents add 6% sales tax)* $_____

TOTAL AMOUNT ENCLOSED $_____

Send your check, money order or credit card information to:
(No C.O.D.'s Please)

Please submit all United States & Other Nations orders to:
Garlinghouse Company
174 Oakwood Drive
Glastonbury, CT. 06033
CALL: (800) 235-5700 FAX: (860) 659-5692

Please Submit all Canadian plan orders to:
Garlinghouse Company
102 Ellis Street
Penticton, BC V2A 4L5
CALL: (800) 361-7526 FAX: (250) 493-7526

ADDRESS INFORMATION:

NAME: _____

STREET: _____

CITY: _____

STATE: _____ **ZIP:** _____

DAYTIME PHONE: _____

EMAIL ADDRESS: _____

Credit Card Information	
Charge To: ❏ Visa	❏ Mastercard
Card # ⎪⎪⎪⎪⎪⎪⎪⎪⎪⎪⎪⎪⎪⎪⎪⎪⎪	
Signature _____ Exp. ____/____	

Payment must be made in U.S. funds. Foreign Mail Orders: Certified bank checks in U.S. funds only
TERMS OF SALE FOR HOME PLANS: All home plans sold through this publication are copyright protected. Reproduction of these home plans, either in whole or in part, including any direct copying and/or preparation of derivative works thereof, for any reason without the prior written permission of Garlinghouse, Inc., is strictly prohibited. The purchase of a set of home plans in no way transfers any copyright or other ownership interest in it to the buyer except for a limited license to use that set of home plans for the construction of one, and only one, dwelling unit. The purchase of additional sets of that home plan at a reduced price from the original set or as a part of a multiple set package does not entitle the buyer with a license to construct more than one dwelling unit.

Privacy Statement (please read)

Dear Valued Garlinghouse Customer,

Your privacy is extremely important to us. We'd like to take a little of your time to explain our privacy policy.

As a service to you, we would like to provide your name to companies such as the following:

- Building material manufacturers that we are affiliated with. Who would like to keep you current with their product line and specials.
- Building material retailers who would like to offer you competitive prices to help you save money.
- Financing companies who would like to offer you competitive mortgage rates.

In addition, as our valued customer, we would like to send you newsletters to assist your building experience. *We* would appreciate your feedback with a customer service survey to improve our operations.

You have total control over the use of your contact information. You can let us know exactly how you want to be contacted. Please check all boxes that apply. Thank you.

   ☐ Don't mail
   ☐ Don't call
   ☐ Don't email
   ☐ Only send Garlinghouse newsletters and customer
   ☐ service surveys

In closing, Garlinghouse is committed to providing superior customer service and protection of your privacy. We thank you for your time and consideration.

Sincerely,

James D. McNair III
CEO

For Our USA Customers:
Order Toll Free — 1-800-235-5700
Monday-Friday 8:00 a.m. to 8:00 p.m. Eastern Time
or FAX your Credit Card order to 1-860-659-5692
All foreign residents call 1-860-659-5667

For Our Canadian Customers:
Order Toll Free — 1-800-361-7526
Monday-Friday 8:00 a.m. to 5:00 p.m. Pacific Time
or FAX your Credit Card order to 1-250-493-7526
Customer Service: 1-250-493-0942

Please have ready: 1. Your credit card number 2. The plan number 3. The order code number ⇨ **H2SL9**

Garlinghouse 2002 Blueprint Price Code Schedule

	1 Set	4 Sets	8 Sets	Vellums	ML	Itemized ZIP Quote
A	$345	$385	$435	$525	$60	$50
B	$375	$415	$465	$555	$60	$50
C	$410	$450	$500	$590	$60	$50
D	$450	$490	$540	$630	$60	$50
E	$495	$535	$585	$675	$70	$60
F	$545	$585	$635	$725	$70	$60
G	$595	$635	$685	$775	$70	$60
H	$640	$680	$730	$820	$70	$60
I	$685	$725	$775	$865	$80	$70
J	$725	$765	$815	$905	$80	$70
K	$765	$805	$855	$945	$80	$70
L	$800	$840	$890	$980	$80	$70

Shipping — (Plans 1-59999)	1-3 Sets	4-6 Sets	7+ & Vellums
Standard Delivery (UPS 2-Day)	$25.00	$30.00	$35.00
Overnight Delivery	$35.00	$40.00	$45.00

Shipping — (Plans 60000-99999)	1-3 Sets	4-6 Sets	7+ & Vellums
Ground Delivery (7-10 Days)	$15.00	$20.00	$25.00
Express Delivery (3-5 Days)	$20.00	$25.00	$30.00

International Shipping & Handling	1-3 Sets	4-6 Sets	7+ & Vellums
Regular Delivery Canada (7-10 Days)	$25.00	$30.00	$35.00
Express Delivery Canada (5-6 Days)	$40.00	$45.00	$50.00
Overseas Delivery Airmail (2-3 Weeks)	$50.00	$60.00	$65.00

Additional sets with original order $50

IMPORTANT INFORMATION TO READ BEFORE YOU PLACE YOUR ORDER

How Many Sets Of Plans Will You Need?

The Standard 8-Set Construction Package

*Our experience shows that you'll speed every step of construction and avoid costly building errors by ordering enough sets to go around. Each tradesperson wants a set — the general contractor and all subcontractors; foundation, electrical, plumbing, heating/air conditioning and framers. Don't forget your lending institution, building department and, of course, a set for yourself. * Recommended For Construction **

The Minimum 4-Set Construction Package

*If you're comfortable with arduous follow-up, this package can save you a few dollars by giving you the option of passing down plan sets as work progresses. You might have enough copies to go around if work goes exactly as scheduled and no plans are lost or damaged by subcontractors. But for only $60 more, the 8-set package eliminates these worries. *Recommended For Bidding **

The Single Study Set

We offer this set so you can study the blueprints to plan your dream home in detail. They are stamped "study set only-not for construction", and you cannot build a home from them. In pursuant to copyright laws, it is illegal to reproduce any blueprint.

Our Reorder and Exchange Policies:

If you find after your initial purchase that you require additional sets of plans you may purchase them from us at special reorder prices (please call for pricing details) provided that you reorder within 6 months of your original order date. There is a $28 reorder processing fee that is charged on all reorders. For more information on reordering plans please contact our Customer Service Department. Your plans are custom printed especially for you once you place your order. For that reason we cannot accept any returns. If for some reason you find that the plan you have purchased from us does not meet your needs, then you may exchange that plan for any other plan in our collection. We allow you sixty days from your original invoice date to make an exchange. At the time of the exchange you will be charged a processing fee of 20% of the total amount of your original order plus the difference in price between the plans (if applicable) plus the cost to ship the new plans to you. Call our Customer Service Department for more information. Please Note: Reproducible vellums can only be exchanged if they are unopened.

Important Shipping Information

Please refer to the shipping charts on the order form for service availability for your specific plan number. Our delivery service must have a street address or Rural Route Box number — never a post office box. (PLEASE NOTE: Supplying a P.O. Box number only will delay the shipping of your order.) Use a work address if no one is home during the day. Orders being shipped to APO or FPO must go via First Class Mail. Please include the proper postage.

For our International Customers, only Certified bank checks and money orders are accepted and must be payable in U.S. currency. For speed, we ship international orders Air Parcel Post. Please refer to the chart for the correct shipping cost.

Important Canadian Shipping Information

To our friends in Canada, we have a plan design affiliate in Penticton, BC. This relationship will help you avoid the delays and charges associated with shipments from the United States. Moreover, our affiliate is familiar with the building requirements in your community and country. We prefer payments in U.S. Currency. If you, however, are sending Canadian funds please add 45% to the prices of the plans and shipping fees.

An Important Note About Building Code Requirements:

All plans are drawn to conform to one or more of the industry's major national building standards. However, due to the variety of local building regulations, your plan may need to be modified to comply with local requirements — snow loads, energy loads, seismic zones, etc. Do check them fully and consult your local building officials.

A few states require that all building plans used be drawn by an architect registered in that state. While having your plans reviewed and stamped by such an architect may be prudent, laws requiring non-conforming plans like ours to be completely redrawn forces you to unnecessarily pay very large fees. If your state has such a law, we strongly recommend you contact your state representative to protest.

The rendering, floor plans and technical information contained within this publication are not guaranteed to be totally accurate. Consequently, no information from this publication should be used either as a guide to constructing a home or for estimating the cost of building a home. Complete blueprints must be purchased for such purposes.

Index

Option Key

BL	Bottom-line Zip Quote	**ML**	Materials List Available	**ZIP**	Itemized Zip Quote	**RRR**	Right Reading Reverse	**DUP**	Duplex Plan

TOP SELLING
GARAGE PLANS

Save money by Doing-It-Yourself using our Easy-To-Follow plans. Whether you intend to build your own garage or contract it out to a building professional, the Garlinghouse garage plans provide you with everything you need to price out your project and get started. Put our 90+ years of experience to work for you. Order now!!

No. 06016C   **$86.00**
Apartment Garage With One Bedroom

No. 06015C   **$86.00**
Apartment Garage With Two Bedrooms

- 24' x 28' Overall Dimensions
- 544 Square Foot Apartment
- 12/12 Gable Roof with Dormers
- Slab or Stem Wall Foundation Options

- 26' x 28' Overall Dimensions
- 728 Square Foot Apartment
- 4/12 Pitch Gable Roof
- Slab or Stem Wall Foundation Options

No. 06012C   **$54.00**
30' Deep Gable &/or Eave Jumbo Garages

- 4/12 Pitch Gable Roof
- Available Options for Extra Tall Walls, Garage & Personnel Doors, Foundation, Window, & Sidings
- Package contains 4 Different Sizes
- 30' x 28'   • 30' x 32'   • 30' x 36'   • 30' x 40'

No. 06013C   **$68.00**
Two-Car Garage With Mudroom/Breezeway

- Attaches to Any House
- 24' x 24' Eave Entry
- Available Options for Utility Room with Bath, Mudroom, Screened-In Breezeway, Roof, Foundation, Garage & Personnel Doors, Window, & Sidings

No. 06001C   **$48.00**

12', 14' & 16' Wide-Gable 1-Car Garages

- Available Options for Roof, Foundation, Window, Door, & Sidings
- Package contains 8 Different Sizes
- 12' x 20' Mini-Garage • 14' x 22' • 16' x 20' • 16' x 24'
- 14' x 20'   • 14' x 24' • 16' x 22' • 16' x 26'

No. 06003C   **$48.00**

24' Wide-Gable 2-Car Garages

- Available Options for Side Shed, Roof, Foundation, Garage & Personnel Doors, Window, & Sidings
- Package contains 5 Different Sizes
- 24' x 22'   • 24' x 24'   • 24' x 26'
- 24' x 28'   • 24' x 32'

No. 06007C   **$60.00**

Gable 2-Car Gambrel Roof Garages

- Interior Rear Stairs to Loft Workshop
- Front Loft Cargo Door With Pulley Lift
- Available Options for Foundation, Garage & Personnel Doors, Window, & Sidings
- Package contains 5 Different Sizes
- 22' x 26' • 22' x 28' • 24' x 28' • 24' x 30' • 24' x 32'

No. 06006C   **$48.00**

22' & 24' Deep Eave 2 & 3-Car Garages

- Can Be Built Stand-Alone or Attached to House
- Available Options for Roof, Foundation, Garage & Personnel Doors, Window, & Sidings
- Package contains 6 Different Sizes
- 22' x 28'   • 22' x 32'   • 24' x 32'
- 22' x 30'   • 24' x 30'   • 24' x 36'

No. 06002C   **$48.00**

20' & 22' Wide-Gable 2-Car Garages

- Available Options for Roof, Foundation, Garage & Personnel Doors, Window, & Sidings
- Package contains 7 Different Sizes
- 20' x 20'   • 20' x 24'   • 22' x 22'   • 22' x 28'
- 20' x 22'   • 20' x 28'   • 22' x 24'

No. 06008C   **$60.00**

Eave 2 & 3-Car Clerestory Roof Garages

- Interior Side Stairs to Loft Workshop
- Available Options for Engine Lift, Foundation, Garage & Personnel Doors, Window, & Sidings
- Package contains 4 Different Sizes
- 24' x 26'   • 24' x 28'   • 24' x 32'   • 24' x 36'

Order Code No: **H2SL9**

Garage Order Form

Please send me 3 complete sets of the following
GARAGE PLAN BLUEPRINTS:

Item no. & description	Price
Additional Sets	$ _____
(@ $10.00 EACH)	$ _____
Garage Vellum	
(@ $200.00 EACH)	$ _____
Shipping Charges: UPS-$3.75, First Class-$4.50	$ _____
Subtotal:	$ _____
Resident sales tax: CT-6% (NOT REQUIRED FOR OTHER STATES)	$ _____

Total Enclosed: $ _____

My Billing Address is:

Name: _____

Address: _____

City: _____

State: _____ Zip: _____

Daytime Phone No. (_____) _____

My Shipping Address is:

Name: _____

Address: _____
(UPS will not ship to P.O. Boxes)

City: _____

State: _____ Zip: _____

For Faster Service...Charge It!
U.S. & Canada Call
1(800)235-5700

All foreign residents call 1(860)659-5667
MASTERCARD, VISA

Card # | | | | | | | | | | | | | |

Signature _____ Exp. ____/____

If paying by credit card, to avoid delays:
billing address must be as it appears on credit card statement
or FAX us at (860) 659-5692

Here's What You Get

- Three complete sets of drawings for each plan ordere
- Detailed step-by-step instructions with easy-to-follow diagrams on how to build your garage (not available with apartment garages)
- For each garage style, a variety of size and garage door configuration options
- Variety of roof styles and/or pitch options for most garages
- Complete materials list
- Choice between three foundation options: Monolithic Slab, Concrete Stem Wall or Concrete Block Stem Wa
- Full framing plans, elevations and cross-sectionals for each garage size and configuration

Garage Plan Blueprints

All blueprint garage plan orders contain three complete sets of drawings with instructions and are priced as listed next to the illustration. **These blueprint garage plans can not be modified.** Additional sets of plans may be obtained for $10.00 each with your original order. UPS shipping is used unless otherwise requested. Please include the proper amount for shipping.

Garage Plan Vellums

By purchasing vellums for one of our garage plans, you receive one vellum set of the same construction drawings found in the blueprints, but printed on vellum paper. Vellums can be erased and are perfect for making design changes. They are also semi-transparent making them easy to duplicate. But most importantly, the purchase o garage plan vellums comes with a broader license that allows you to make changes to the design (ie, create a hand drawn or CAD derivative work), to make copies o the plan and to build one garage from the plan.

Send your order to:
(With check or money order payable in U.S. funds only)
The Garlinghouse Company
174 Oakwood Drive
Glastonbury, CT 06033

No C.O.D. orders accepted; U.S. funds only. UPS will not ship to Post Office boxes, FPO boxes, APO boxes, Alaska or Hawaii. Canadian orders must be shipped First Class.

Prices subject to change without notice.